Praise for
The Ovarian Chronicles

"Reading *The Ovarian Chronicles* felt like I was allowing myself to breathe. Sometimes it felt as if Cat was reading my mind, sometimes it read like deeply touching poetry, and sometimes the wisdom hit me right between the eyes. This is not a self-help book but a journey that feels like we are walking together through pain, grieving, hope and miracles. All women should read and breathe in Cat's story so we can support each other more fully through this adventure, with potholes and hills, called life."

~ Marcia Reynolds, PsyD, author of *Wander Woman,*
The Discomfort Zone and *Outsmart Your Brain*

"Cat Williford in *The Ovarian Chronicles* evokes the soul, the magic, wisdom and resiliency of our collective feminine spirit. From the delivery of the news one would never want to hear from a gynecologist, to battling layers of grief and finally listening to her body's inner knowing, Cat shares her story with honesty, humor and deep love and helps us awaken to the call of our own body's wisdom. Through her heartfelt stories, this book will be a rally cry for women everywhere to listen to their innate wisdom and be courageous in their pursuit to do what's right for them!"

~ Agapi Stassinopoulos, author of *Wake Up to the Joy of You* and *Unbinding the Heart*

"When it comes to fertility, medical facts are just one part of the story. Cat shows us how to listen, hear and live into other sides of this multifaceted story. She shares her own narrative of challenging the science and searching for balance. Through her story Cat explores duty to self and the need for real relationship. She reveals how women can truly support each other. At the heart of this book is the importance of understanding and valuing the link between our emotions, hormones, mind and body. How emotions get locked into our bodies and impact our health and wellbeing, until we do the work to unlock them and set ourselves free. Cat's remarkable and inspiring journey is of a powerfully self-aware writer who shows the way for other women to discover and accept who we truly are."

~ Helen Caton, author, *The Fertility Plan*

"After wiping the tears of emotion from my eyes, both tears of laughter and tears of grief, I can say unequivocally that this book shares the deep soul of being a woman, with the many challenges a woman experiences. Written in the incredibly straightforward "Texas" voice of Cat Williford, I would recommend this book to all women and to all men who want to understand women better."

~ Henry Kimsey-House, Co-Founder of CTI and Co-Author of *Co-Active Coaching, Co-Active Leadership,* and *The Stake*

"Every woman who has struggled with the joys and disappointments of our own bodies (and that's ALL of us) will find points of identification with Cat Williford's *The Ovarian Chronicles*. Cat brings humor, charm, and rawness to a uniquely female experience. From family, partners and fertility, to the falling in love we must all do with ourselves, Cat brilliantly shares her journey while offering a pathway for each of us to mend the big rifts inside of us. She bridges the gaps between commonsense, magic and reality as she invites us to take charge of our health, our bodies beautiful and our life."

~ Morgana Rae, author of *Financial Alchemy: 12 Months of Magic & Manifestation*, co-host of "Crazy Sexy Midlife Love" radio

"In *The Ovarian Chronicles*, author Cat Williford captures the essence of being a woman. From what we do for love to what we do when love unravels, from how we handle our fertility and scary words at a doctor's office to our womanly grief, Cat shares a magic-filled and sacred blueprint for the profound journey back to joy. This book touched me deeply and connected me to my own rich, terrifying and beautiful journey as a woman. You'll love this book and want to give a copy to all your girlfriends."

~ Karen Kimsey-House, Co-founder of CTI, and Co-Author of *Co-Active Coaching, Co-Active Leadership*, and *Integration*

The *Ovarian* Chronicles

Expectations • Heartache • Resilience

CAT WILLIFORD

Putnam & Smith Publishing Company

The Ovarian Chronicles by Cat Williford.

Edited by: Mary Reynolds Thompson and Sheila Kennedy
Cover and Book Design by: Michelle Radomski
Photography by: Jolie Margulies

A Note To The Reader
This is a memoir. Neither the publisher nor the author is engaged in rendering professional advice or services to the individual reader. The ideas, procedures, alternative-healing experiences of the author in this book are not intended as a substitute for consulting with your physician. All matters regarding your health require medical supervision. Neither the author nor the publisher shall be liable or responsible for any loss, injury, or damage allegedly arising from any information or implied suggestion in this book.

Distributed by:
Putnam & Smith Publishing Company
15915 Ventura Boulevard, Suite 101
Encino, California 91436

www.putnamandsmithpublishing.com

Library of Congress Control Number: 2020945372

ISBN: 978-1-939986-28-3

Printed in the United States of America

For All Women:
Past, Present and Future

Table of Contents

Introduction

Truth: There is no such thing as "doing everything right."

Wisdom: Doing everything you can in the moment, with as much optimism and love as you can muster, is more important than doing everything right.

Truth: Waiting for a day can turn into waiting for a few months, which can turn into years when you love someone. You get busy with life, celebrating one New Year's Eve after another. You recognize the passage of time but not always the significance of its passing or the possible repercussions of waiting. Years zoom by without your paying much attention to them.

Wisdom: The waiting can cost you a dream, or two.

Why did I wait until I was forty-one to put my foot down with Rich and say to him and the Universe, "Yes, now, baby please," like I was ordering a chocolate shake from a Dairy Queen drive-thru? Moments had turned into years in our live-for-today household, stuffed full with three dogs (our fur-babies) and a consistent flow of clients, friends and family.

Why did I ignore more seasoned women's encouragement to take my baby stand while I was in my early and mid thirties? Perhaps the answer is because my inherent optimism slid easily into believing a little too much in the happy Hollywood finale. While optimism is great, the sneaky Fairytale Fine mask erects and buries your fears and vulnerability deeper and deeper until you can't really feel them anymore. Optimism also means pretending that you will get what you want after you help him get what he wants. Because you believe you are a good person and good things come to those who wait. That's when the Suck It Up Buttercup mask is born and stuffs the inner longing rising up at an inconvenient time . . . for someone else. You recognize the passage of time but not always the significance of its passing or the possible repercussions of waiting. Under the masks, years zoom by without your paying much attention to the possible repercussions.

Breaking silence inside that forever relationship feels scary. You must be prepared to walk or lose forever the hope of your dream's promise. And so you wait. And you wait some more. You hide your fears and vulnerability deeper and deeper beneath that Fairytale Fine mask. And you gain weight in the waiting. And you lose weight in the waiting. And your attention strays to another. In the middle of an emotional outburst about how someone bagged the groceries you discover that you've been pushing down the frustration and lie that it will be my turn one day under the Suck It Up Buttercup mask. And because you are raised to be a good and loyal person, you keep waiting, even though you are suffocating under the weighty masks.

And sometimes (maybe even often), the pain and frustration of putting your dreams second to someone else's, even someone you love passionately, winds up as a crisis in your body. Maybe not immediately, but eventually it shows up.

So even though you like to do the right thing, it is never about doing everything right. The struggle is finding the balance between what feels right and good in the moment, and ultimately awakening to what is for your highest good.

Waking up may or may not make a dream come true. But it does force you to live authentically, free of the masks hiding what has become your deepest pain. It burns like the last strokes of swimming the length of an Olympic size pool while holding your breath. The exhale releases the pent-up toxic build up. It is on that exhale that you learn to align mind, body, heart and soul. And in that exhale process? Oh, the learning. Oh, the healing.

A Note to the Reader

This is a memoir. The people in my life didn't get together and say, "Hey, write your story and be sure to include me in it!" So, some names and locations have been changed in order to provide privacy and anonymity.

CHAPTER 1

Diagnosis

My feet in the stirrups with a baby blue paper sheet covering my half nakedness, I watched Dr. K point to the ultrasound screen with a furrowed brow. With her nose mere inches from the monitor, she said, "I don't like the look of this cyst. It looks un-boring, un-boring enough to warrant removal."

"Un-*boring?*" I wondered aloud, not knowing there were cyst categories: boring and un-boring.

A vaginal ultrasound wand wiggled around inside of me. Six weeks earlier, during a routine check-up, what was thought to be a small cyst was discovered on my right ovary. Neither Dr. K nor I was worried. I'd had many ovarian cysts and they resolved on their own, usually without much fanfare. Aside, of course, from that time in my early twenties when I had a baseball-sized cyst. Surgery had been scheduled and was a week away when, doing a part-time gig as a catering server, I hoisted a way-too-heavy tray above my shoulder and the cyst ruptured. I crumpled to the floor as dirty plates, silverware and glasses went flying. (I never worked for that caterer again.)

There was also the time in my early thirties when a large cyst ruptured on a Sunday night around 9:00 p.m. and my patient-friendly-then-gynecologist said to meet him at his office rather than the ER. The next day I had a noon keynote to deliver—which I did while leaning against the banquet table on stage because I still could not stand upright without wincing. Fortunately, the audience was female and I explained my situation. Later, one of the attendees asked me why I hadn't stayed home. The thought of cancelling never occurred to me.

Dr. K regained my attention explaining, "Cysts are fluid filled and this thing looks solid." She swiveled the monitor so I could see the cyst on the ultrasound screen. "See this?" she asked tapping the screen with her index finger where she wanted me to look, her other hand moving the wand inside me. "Your bladder is fluid filled and dark inside." She moved her finger to the un-boring cyst, "This growth is light hued . . . it looks *tissue* filled," she said knowingly with a sigh, removing the wand. I looked at her puzzled. "Tumor," she said softly.

I knew I was supposed to say something by the way she looked at me but didn't know what, so I followed my mother's habitual advice to me: If you can't say anything nice, don't say anything at all. The not nice inside my head sounded like: "Whatthefuckyou gottabekiddingmeihaven'thadcoffeeyetforcryingoutloudinchurch!"

"During surgery, I'll first baggie the ovary and growth to keep any rupture contained. If it is cancer, we don't want the cells to migrate anywhere else."

I envisioned the baggie in place and wondered if she'd use the twist tie kind or Ziploc. I shook my head, clearing the image,

2

then blinked several times. Had Dr. K just told me that I needed surgery *and might have cancer?*

How could anything that dire possibly be going on inside of me? I don't have any pain. My energy is high. Bloody hell, I just got the all clear in January after a year and a half of wonky PAP tests. Slow down, I mentally intoned. My cysts always rupture, hurt like hell, and resolve themselves . . . *before* the scheduled surgery.

In the middle of my mental rant, I heard her say the word "stages" and I knew it would be impossible to take in any more information or make a wise decision lying on my back under the baby blue paper sheet, feet up in the air, like a dying bug.

With as much grace as I could muster, I lifted my feet out of the stirrups while struggling to cover my nakedness, only to get tangled in the paper sheet. "Of course, you are welcome to see a general surgeon or another gynecologist for a second opinion."

Oblivious to or kindly ignoring my sheet difficulties, she continued, "Most male surgeons will see your age and also remove the ovary as a precaution. I know what you want . . . and I will do everything I can to save the ovary."

I could feel my eyes squint and forehead squish up, as if trying to read in bright sunlight. Dr. K stopped talking, perhaps realizing that I wasn't taking in her words.

I felt cold. I felt hot. I felt like an inferno in a block of ice. I felt the all-too-familiar-with-medical-baggage surgeon's daughter part of me kick in, preparing to ask all the smart medical questions. I felt the tug of my grown woman's holistic approach pulling me away from traditional medicine and toward natural healing. "Reduce coffee intake, Cat," I mentally noted.

Dr. K had been my doctor for fifteen years. She is non-alarmist and conservative when it comes to advising procedures, and I trusted her. I wasn't compelled to seek out another surgeon. Having spent years listening to my equally non-alarmist surgeon father talk about surgery, cancer, and tumor removal, I knew the word "growth" wasn't something to ignore. "The only way to know if it's malignant is to take it out and put it under the microscope," my father would say. I thought about the aftermath of my grandmother's chemo and radiation—her exhaustion, lack of appetite, hair loss. And yet, she ultimately won her battle with cancer and lived to celebrate her ninety-fourth birthday.

I nodded to let Dr. K know I could hear her, even though I was, in fact, caught between trying to listen and trying not to listen as she prattled on about preferred hospitals and the procedural difference between laparoscopic and regular incision methods. The surgical procedures played out in Technicolor before my eyes, and I flinched as I envisioned the steely blade cutting into my abdomen. She described the ease of removal, potential risks, and the size and severity of the scars depending on each method.

"Scar size is the least of my concerns," I said; my left hand gently caressing the nearly invisible scar that wraps around the right side of my waist, where my kidney once resided. I donated that kidney to my beloved daddy, and I wear the scar like a badge of honor. Touching it, I felt like I could overcome anything. After all, hadn't I survived the devastating loss of him, in spite of having given him my youthful, healthy kidney? Hadn't I persevered and overcome the injuries after the drunken boy whose car I was in, plowed us straight into a train, the kind of accident most do not survive? Hadn't I waterskied that summer, in spite of the orthopedic doctor's prognosis? I also learned to wear a seatbelt and not get in cars with inebriated teenage boys.

Once again fueled with my natural defiance, I sought to believe surgery would be unnecessary.

"I'm on spring break next week with the kids, so we'll schedule surgery for the following week. Joan will call you with the details." Still seated on her rolling stool, Dr. K patted my baby-blue-paper-sheet-covered knee and smiled as she said, "The good news is we are catching this early if anything is going on." I tried to hold at bay the vision of me bald.

Staring at a poster about birth control on the opposite wall, I thought back to the beginning of the year. Then, the growth was tiny and assumed to be a benign cyst. It would have been a normal course of action to put me on the pill for a few months, but Dr. K and I agreed that was not the best thing for me. The pill triggers my migraines. Worse still, it is supposed to *prevent* pregnancy.

After a moment of silence, I said, "I don't feel like this is life-threatening. I am terrified it is fertility-threatening." My voice cracked on the word fertility and a lone tear escaped, despite my locked jaw.

One hand still on my knee, she used her other hand to hold mine, and looked me straight in the eyes. "I will do *everything* I can to save your ovary. I promise you. But my first priority is your overall health."

While it is true many a woman has gotten pregnant with only one ovary, I knew my chances were already slim. My FSH (Follicle Stimulating Hormone—the badass hormone that tells an ovary to release an egg each month) was already in short supply. In our twenties, our FSH is abundant. It begins to dwindle in our thirties and then gets lazier as perimenopause and menopause set in. Blood tests revealed my chances of getting pregnant were not impossible, just low. After howling and sobbing over that test result, I decided to count on my lifelong luck, hoping it had not run out. To boost my belief I read all the articles in celebrity magazines with headlines shouting out, "Miracle baby for . . . " forty-something so-and-so in grocery store checkout lines and while getting pedicures.

As Dr. K talked of saving my ovary, I actually had no idea if either or both of my ovaries were still releasing eggs during each month's cycle. I only knew that my entire being latched leech-like onto her promise to give me every piece of luck I could get. She stood up, and before leaving the room, gave me a side-by-side shoulder hug. That hug made me feel like we were in this together.

Alone, I sat on the edge of the exam table, staring at the floor, realizing why Dr. K is always running late. She cares. Irritation about all the time spent in her waiting room vanished. No doubt, given her specialty, her next patient was a fertility patient. The word "fertility" lodged in my brain and waves of disappointment, self-loathing and utter despair washed through me as I asked myself the same damn question I had asked myself hundreds of times of late, "Why did you wait, Cat? Why, why, why?" I had no answer that would bring me peace or change the circumstances.

I couldn't move; it seemed like my bottom was super-glued to the white paper atop the exam table. Before I could stop the freight train of responsible-to-others-no-matter-what thoughts, they rolled, picking up steam along the way. They began with the incredibly exciting Leadership training course in Toronto my dear friend and colleague Cyndi had asked me to collaborate on. Oh my God, what if I can't deliver the workshop with her at the end of April? The tickets were all booked, including the one from Toronto directly to Houston to help my mom prep for my brother's wedding in New Orleans, my bridesmaid dress already ordered and set to arrive at my mom's house just before I did.

The knock on the door startled me, and I jumped up ripping the white paper under me. "Just a minute," I said and took a breath. Starting to get dressed, the thoughts continued. I wouldn't dare miss my beloved brother's wedding (his second wedding to my none); realizing quickly I was comparing myself to my five years older brother, like I did when he had two diplomas (high school and undergrad) before I was even a Senior in high school. I sure as heck was not going to let Cyndi down or miss out on the opportunity to do what I do best—facilitate learning. What am I doing? I asked myself zipping up my jeans, suddenly aware of their tightness across my right ovary. And then, a quick flash of insight: Cat, how about you make you and your health *the* priority?

I began to shake with dry-heaves and my heart torched and scorched a hole in my chest. The last time I made me a priority . . .

"OhMyGodOhMyGodOhMyGod—I can't go through another heartbreak right now," my mind shrieked. I grabbed the back of a chair to keep from buckling. My eyes welled up. I clenched my jaw to stop from crying and under my breath repeated the mandate to myself, "Hang on, hang on, *hang on*. Just get to the car."

I smiled thinly at the reception team on my way out. They smiled back at me with a mixture of sympathy and weariness.

I'd seen that same cancer fatigue on my father's face too many times. Now those smiles squeezed my tender stomach flesh so hard I felt like vomiting. I swallowed bile and managed a fake smile back.

Melting into the seat of my car, I dug my phone out of my purse and watched my hands shake while speed-dialing one of my besties, Veronica, praying that she wasn't in a meeting and would answer her phone. She answered, her tone all business, and I let out my barely contained sobs of fright. Shifting immediately from professional woman into sister-friend, she listened, sighed with me, and uttered all the just right "Oh, honeys."

Veronica is the kind of woman who won't bullshit you and takes tender care of those she loves. Though she works in the medical field, she also gravitates toward holistic healing. I completely trust her intuition and often think she should hang out a "psychic" shingle. "Do you sense this is really something to be worried about?" I asked. We sat in digital silence for a moment as she breathed deeply, then exhaled the words I longed to hear, "No, I don't get that."

"Oh, thank God. Me neither." I took a deep breath and exhaled fully, realizing I hadn't breathed normally for twenty minutes. Then a flash of my own intuition tumbled out, "I just got something . . . this growth is my grief . . . sadness . . . and friggin' regret coming out physically." We both knew I was talking about the torturous breakup of my seventeen-year relationship with my beloved Rich. Even though several years had passed since we split, in many ways I was still in shock. In spite of all the love, we just hadn't been able to get across the hump that I wanted a child and he

8

decided he didn't. Well, that was the straw that broke that tired and disillusioned relationship's back.

I found love again and was now in a relationship with Scott, a man who from the start said he wanted to be everything to me that Rich couldn't be—he wanted to be my husband and baby daddy. It was partially Scott's boyish optimism, distrust of statistics, and his mind over matter approach that helped me override the low FSH number after I told him what it was. So why had the growth shown up at *this* moment? Hadn't I exited that cave of grief? Or was my body telling me there was still more pain to surrender?

I called Scott next, and he didn't answer. "Hey, I need surgery because I might have cancer," is not a good message to leave someone. Instead, sounding like the wreck of the Hesperus and more than a little cryptic, I opted for, "Call me."

Driving to my second appointment of the day I ached to be able to call my daddy and ask him what he thought. I wanted to hear his love and protection in that soothing voice of his with its southern charm bedside manner. I wanted him to tell me to come home and he'd make it all better.

"Really Cat? You're forty-four and want your daddy to take care of this as if it were a scraped knee like when you were seven years old?" You bet I did.

CHAPTER 2

The
Surgeon's Daughter

The afternoon of my father's life-threatening blood pressure spike, I was eight years old and wearing the sleeveless aqua and white tropical print dress my parents had brought me from Hawaii. Daddy's eyes were blood-shot red rather than blue, his nose wouldn't stop bleeding and he kept fainting. Mom took him to the doctor and when they came home my father settled into his enormous recliner with an ice pack held to his nose.

My mother's olive skin, normally very tan, appeared ashen and, from where I sat at the table, I could see my daddy lying very still in the recliner. She said they had to take a trip to Galveston right away, and that she and Daddy would be gone for a while. Luckily, Mam-Maw, my paternal grandmother just happened to be visiting that week and she stayed on to take care of Frank, my big brother who was thirteen, and me.

My brother loaded the suitcases in the trunk and I watched daddy lean on my mother as they walked slowly to the car. He stretched out across the wide back seat of the giant four-door navy blue Buick with a cold, fresh, wet washcloth over his still bleeding nose.

With one arm around my brother and the other one around me, Mom said, "Be good. Do what your grandmother tells you to. And don't worry. Everything is going to be fine." Her voice sounded high pitched and thin rather than her normal smooth alto. She hugged and kissed us and slid into the driver's seat. My grandmother, brother, and I stood in the driveway, watching the car drive away. Though I was only eight years old, I knew life had just changed in a very dramatic way.

It felt as if my parents were gone a year, but they came home just three weeks later with the diagnosis malignant hypertension. My thirty-nine-year-old father was thirty pounds lighter and my mom was, well, different; thinner and smoking more. She hovered over all of us, as if by her close proximity, she could keep us safe.

From that day forward, my worry for my father grew. I didn't know what hypertension was but knew my daddy's was usually kept under control with a daily handful of pills. Even so, as his body adjusted to the new medication, at times he'd crumple into a heap in the kitchen or den if those pills drove his blood pressure too low. I also knew that his weight was involved somehow. He'd try to eat less of everything but in particular, fried chicken, BBQ ribs and steak, and anything salty, but then his old urges would emerge. With each rise and fall in weight, his blood pressure spiked or dropped, and the medication would change again.

When I came of age in the late 1970's and early 1980's, stress wasn't the buzzword it is today. Men of my father's generation didn't verbalize emotional burdens like stress, and they didn't complain. None of us knew back then how to talk with him about the obvious: the pressure of people's lives being literally in his hands in the operating room every day. His job required a ferocious focus and willingness to make big decisions. One wrong move or slip of the hand could kill someone. Yet, he *loved* being a surgeon. Though one of his pet peeves irked him to no end: patients telling him what surgery they needed! "Doc, you gotta take out my gallbladder. It's killing me." He used to joke that he wanted to send them to Nick's, the local market and butcher shop a block from his office to pick up a spicy, stuffed pork chop and eat it for dinner. "Call me after you eat it. If you love it and want another one the next day, you don't need your gallbladder removed. If you are in pain, come back and see me." Of course he never followed through on his joke, but he delighted in it nonetheless.

The greenhouse he built in the backyard still stands. His way of decompressing after a tough day in the OR was to put his hands in the dirt. We could gauge just how tough his day had been by how long he spent with his tomatoes, jalapeno peppers, okra, eggplant, cucumbers and squash or if there was a second cocktail before dinner. He subscribed to the magazine *Organic Gardener* in the 1980's, way before organic was cool.

After college, every time I returned to L.A. from a visit home, I had the sickening thought: I might not ever see Daddy again. Once, before leaving, I tried to convince him to do something about his health—lose weight, stop drinking, become a patient of a doctor he couldn't manipulate. "And when did you get your medical degree?" he asked, his usual words to end a conversation about his health. I spent the first segment of my flight back to L.A. that day in the bathroom wailing. The second half of my return flight I spent drinking. Like father like daughter.

At my cousin's wedding, everyone in the family saw the effects of my father's long-term hypertension, and that they were getting worse. His body was bloated and there was a near-constant exhausted look on his face. We silently marveled and whispered prayers of thanks at how he kept going.

Back in L.A., on a gorgeous Saturday summer afternoon while on a sort-of-date's sailboat in Marina Del Rey, preparing to sail into Santa Monica Bay, a feeling of dread swept over me. I looked at Howard and said, "I need a phone. Where's the nearest phone?" He pointed to a bank of phones near the marina's bathhouse.

I leapt off the boat and jogged as quickly as I could in flip-flops to the phones. I called my Hollywood apartment's answering machine to check messages. My fingers fumbled punching in the code, like I couldn't remember it. Finally the long beep, and then I heard, "You have one message." The feeling of apprehension climbed several notches.

"Crap, I don't have a pen and paper," I said out loud, fishing in the pockets of my white shorts for a lipstick—anything to write on my hand with. I felt dizzy.

"Hi Cat. It's Frank. Daddy is in ICU. I've booked a ticket for you first thing in the morning. Call me at Park Place and ask for the ICU nurse's desk. They know to come get me. I'll give you the confirmation number then."

There it was. The call I'd been afraid of since I'd gone away to college. I slid down the wall and collapsed into tears on the splintery planks of the dock. I flailed a bit as Howard tried to hug me then relaxed into his arms, still crying.

He tried his best to convince me to get back on the boat and go sailing—that there was nothing I could do that afternoon but sit and stew, so I might as well enjoy the beautiful day. I looked at him like he had nineteen heads.

From the pay phone, I called Frank at the hospital as Howard closed up the sailboat's cabin. My brother is an even-keeled, fairly unflappable guy. The tightness and fear in his voice told me he thought Daddy might be dying.

Howard brought my purse to me and sliding into his car I said, "The irony is, my daddy would love this kind of day on the water. He'd probably tell me to go enjoy it. But I can't."

Once home, I packed, arranged for a ride to the airport and let my work friend (who also was part owner of the company) know I would not be coming in the next week. I could not sleep. I tried to pray. I locked my thoughts onto all the other times my daddy had come through, despite what the doctors said.

My brother picked me up at the airport and on the short ride to the hospital tried to prepare me for what I was going to see. He also said mom was home trying to nap, as she'd sat up with Daddy the night before. He parked the car in the doctor's parking lot, and we went in the doctor's back door leading straight into ICU. I'd walked down that ICU hallway quietly hundreds of times. Suddenly, it all looked very unfamiliar.

Frank paused outside a door and I saw "Williford" on the name placard. "Are you ready?" he asked. I nodded my head not at all sure I was.

We walked in. My daddy was sleeping. Tubes and wires seemed to cover him and monitors with constantly fluctuating numbers surrounded his head. He was ghostly gray and looked lifeless. I grabbed my brother's strong arm as I began to fall over into a faint. He caught me and put me in the ugly gold high back chair my mom had tried to sleep in the night before.

When I came to, a nurse offered me a cup of water, and I asked as I looked at my father, "What's wrong?"

"His kidneys are failing," she said with a strange combination of tenderness and matter-of-factness.

"Well give him one of mine then," I blurted, beginning to sob.

At fifty-four my father was in kidney failure. Malignant hypertension had finally exacted its toll on his body. An ultrasound revealed his kidneys were small for a man his size. He didn't weigh four pounds when he was born prematurely and spent his first months in an incubator. And now, his doctors feared he was beyond dialysis. He needed a transplant.

Though I was delirious from travel, exhaustion, and worry when I said, "Well give him one of mine then," I spoke those words with the clarity and certainty that intuition instills. Once again, my father miraculously rebounded from this stay in ICU. But twice-weekly dialysis proved to be too wearying and stamina depleting for a surgeon. Though completely morose about it, he had to retire from doing the thing he loved—performing miracles via surgery. Eighteen months after I first uttered, "Well give him one of mine then," the doctor's fears proved true about dialysis not keeping pace. While home visiting for the Christmas holiday, a battery of tests revealed I was a *perfect* match.

The night we found out I was a perfect match, I was writing in my journal in my childhood bedroom and heard my parents talking in their bedroom. I knocked on their slightly ajar door and pushed it open. My dad stretched out horizontally on the king-size bed, propped up on his right elbow and my mom sat on the foot of the bed. She got up and said, "I think you and your father need to talk about this."

She went downstairs, and I sat in the middle of the king size bed, facing my daddy. He was crying. I began to weep at the sight of his tears.

"Cat, if you have any hesitation, I understand. If you change your mind, I understand. This is a bigger deal than you know. I know what goes on in an OR and this is a big goddamn deal."

"I know," I said, even though I didn't, really. "I've read about what will happen and about how painful the recovery can be. But I heal fast. I'm young. I'm healthy," I said in a tone to reassure both of us.

I paused a moment watching my big, strong, invincible, dodged-a-million-bullets daddy weep. His tears unnerved me. "Why are you crying?"

"It's a hell-of-a-thing to ask your child to do something like this," he said quietly, looking suddenly smaller and older.

"You didn't ask. I offered." He reached for my hand and we looked at each other for a long time, my tears dropping onto his outstretched forearm.

Elated, I felt a calling. My life in L.A. as an actress was not what I dreamed it would be. For three years I had been working for a party design company, going from audition to audition, but I had not landed anything close to a breakout roll. Worse still, I had lost my purpose and direction while waiting for my big break. Though the party design world reminded me of theatre productions, in that we created a "set" for a party, this work was not why I'd hauled myself from what could have been a cozy, comfortable life in my home state of Texas.

As soon as the transplant date was set, my mind related everything to the kidney surgery. I worried that all the partying I'd done in high school and college had somehow rendered my kidneys unsuitable to save Daddy. A happy hour drink with friends induced guilt, like I might be messing up my kidneys. I jokingly rationalized that his body wouldn't know what to do with a teetotal organ and ordered another round.

I shared the news of my upcoming donation with friends, extended family and co-workers. The patriarch of the family-run party company I worked for told me I was an exemplary daughter. My acting school friends confirmed the whole experience would be good for a character study. My dad's two sisters told me how courageous and brave I was. My older cousins told me I was special. Acquaintances told me I was an angel; close friends that I was a role model. A friend of a friend, when told about the upcoming transplant exclaimed, "Well, she's going to Heaven!"

I winced at all that glorification. It felt way too big. "All I'm doing is what needs to be done," was my standard reply. "If my father were in a burning building, I'd do whatever I could to get him out. If he were drowning, I'd jump in and save him." It seemed like a very good thing to do, but certainly not angelic, courageous or extraordinary.

When I was alone, I also prayed the transplant experience would heal some of the hurts between my father and me, two Aries, horns locked, saying things in the heat of the moment. My mom often explained that sometimes parents get angry with their children for no seeming reason, other than the child reminds the parent of the traits they don't like in themselves. I suppose that was true from my end, too. I hated how easily I gave into indulgence and temptations like over-eating and drinking. I didn't like how fast I flew to rage, not yet knowing how to stop reacting with big emotion to triggers. I didn't like how anything less than perfect tore me up inside. I prayed the transplant would be the final truce that my father and I both desperately wanted. And when I let it, donating my kidney felt like that calling to a greater purpose.

The extended family gathered for the transplant and quite frankly, the circus, at the University of Texas' Medical Branch, John Sealy Hospital in Galveston. This was the hospital where I was born while my father was still in medical school. My maternal grandfather, paternal aunt, and a cousin all have birthdays around Memorial Day weekend, and my maternal grandparents' anniversary falls in that same time frame. Our surgeries were scheduled for the Friday of Memorial Day weekend, 1989.

The evening before the transplant surgeries, I received the consent documents you have to sign for any hospital procedure. As I read all the ways my surgery could go wrong and the risks associated with it, I looked at my mom with raised eyebrows and a smirk. She was a nervous wreck. "Are you having second thoughts?" she asked sounding out of breath, looking at me intently. "No, of course not. But there is a lot of crap that can go wrong here," I said as I signed on all the highlighted dotted lines. Daddy walked up to the nurse's station as I finished signing the last consent form and put his arm around me, pulling me close and kissing me on top of the head.

"I just signed mine," he said, pointing to the consent forms in front of me.

"Daddy, if something," he stopped me as he slowly moved his head side to side, as if to say no, nothing will happen, I won't have it, and the time for talking about it all is over.

"Cat, it's time to put your game face on." I looked up and saw his game face lock into place. I wondered if this is what he looked like going into the OR as the surgeon. Probably.

When I woke from surgery, the news was my father's body had received the kidney with no problem and it was already working! Despite experiencing the worst physical pain I'd ever felt, I was overjoyed and wanted to get up and dance in glee. The thought of my daddy feeling good, healthy and vibrant felt better to me than the very good painkilling drugs made me feel.

Saturday just after lunch, the day after the surgeries, the whole family trooped first to my father's room to sing "Happy Birthday" to everyone, and then repeated the trick in my hospital room, before cutting the cake. I didn't want cake, but I did want a hell of a lot more drugs. From my armpit to my hip, my right side felt like it was on fire.

Even more than the birthday and anniversary celebrations, we rejoiced that my father's body took to my kidney and it was already working so well! In spite of my drug-induced fuzziness, I finally felt like I knew why I'd been put on earth. It wasn't to make people laugh or cry cathartically through storytelling with my acting. It was to save my daddy's life. I saved the man who had saved so many others.

The transplant team asked me to stay in Galveston for a month post-op so they could monitor my body's adjustment to one kidney. The weeks my father and I recuperated together I experienced the closeness the transplant brochures talked about.

The love for each other that had always been there shone through, obscuring the prior battles of will. I even allowed myself to take in some of my friends' glorifications of me. Maybe I was good after all?

Two and a half weeks post-op, my father started experiencing pain in his stomach and feeling weak. Tests revealed he didn't need as much of the immune-suppressing anti-rejection drug Cyclosporine as initially thought. I was again overjoyed—my kidney didn't need so much help to work in my daddy's body!

But his pain worsened. So back to the hospital we went to check out the kidney. I have to admit, I covered my fear with anger. I felt betrayed by my kidney. I was mad at my father's body for not being stronger. I was frustrated that there was a delay in what I'd come to think of as "our" recovery, and I was mad at God. How dare this be happening?

When the rest of the tests for the kidney came back normal, my anger evaporated. But phrases like "stomach cancer" and "colon cancer" began floating in the air. Stunned silent, my mom and I sat in the room wide-eyed as my father the surgeon and Dr. Jones, the transplant surgeon and my father's med school buddy, decided the only way to know what was going on was to do an exploratory surgery. Steeped in this lingo since I was a kid, I thought that sounded reasonable. I was just glad the problem had nothing to do with my transplanted kidney. Failure did not feel like an option I could live with.

Three weeks to the date of the transplant surgery, Dr. Jones discovered a rupturing appendix. The infection invaded my father's immune-suppressed body like Sherman tanks. After the emergency appendectomy, the doctor said they'd, " . . . cleaned out all the infection they could, and it looked like we dodged a bullet."

Daddy lay in a post-surgery anesthetic haze, nasal gastric tubes hooked to a canister that received the nasty green looking stuff being pumped from his insides. While fitfully drifting in and out of consciousness, he'd reach up and scratch around his nose, and we'd all jump to guide his hand back to the bed.

My brother and sister-in-law had come to Galveston to be with Mom and me on the afternoon of the surgery. That evening, with daddy finally dozing peacefully through the last effects of anesthesia and a post-op pain reliever and sedative, we were encouraged to get out of the hospital and go for a nice dinner.

Driving along the Galveston Seawall on the way to the restaurant, the four of us all noticed a rare sight – the Gulf of Mexico looked like the Caribbean—a beautiful shade of blue-green. I decided that was a sign that things were looking good because I'd never seen the Gulf look prettier. On the way back to the hospital after dinner, the almost full moon sparkled off the Gulf in a way that enchanted me. I decided it was another good omen.

Saturday morning, daddy was still not fully awake from the anesthesia. We asked the doctor in residence who was doing rounds that morning, "What is going on? Shouldn't he be fully out of the anesthesia by now?" He said, "Sometimes when patients have two surgeries in a short time frame, the effects are harder to clear." His words sounded rational, if a bit weird. My brother and sister-in-law departed, assured by the Resident things were fine.

By early afternoon, Daddy sat on the side of the bed, but was not always making sense. Though very thirsty, he could only suck on ice chips with the nasal-gastric tubes down his throat and nose.

After sucking on half a cup of ice chips, he demanded I get him some iced tea, his favorite daytime beverage.

I told him I couldn't as I reached up to hold his hand from pulling out the NG tube. "God-dammit, Cat. Let me scratch my nose." Tired, frustrated and hurt, I flared, "Fine, pull it out and make them take you back to surgery to reinsert it." So much for that post-transplant relationship bliss I'd been experiencing. The nurses told us he'd pulled out the darn tube in the middle of the night and re-insertion had been traumatic on everyone.

A silent truce was called. He wanted to lie down so I helped him get his legs back on the bed and under the covers. Suddenly he was shivering so we asked for more blankets. My mom and I sat there, worrying, as he dozed erratically. We decided one of us should be there so took turns going to the hospital cafeteria and bathroom.

Around four in the afternoon, my father's face contorted painfully and his body shuddered from head to toe. Mom and I watched while our beloved had some event that we thought might be a seizure. We grabbed a nurse walking by and as soon as she saw my father, she went and got another nurse.

By the time the second nurse arrived, my father lay motion-less. This nurse checked his wrist pulse and denied that anything was wrong, wasting precious time as she repeated what we'd heard earlier. "After surgeries so close together patients have trouble clearing the effects of anesthesia." The first time we heard those words that day, they sounded rational; the second time, ridiculous.

My mother, just beginning her journey to boldness, interrupted and said, "Nonsense. My husband just had a seizure or stroke. If you aren't going to call Ray Jones, I will." The nurse said she would and left to make the call. My mom wasn't satisfied with that and picked up the phone in the room and dialed the private home line of her long-time friends.

Don't ever be in a hospital, not even a teaching one, on a Saturday. Things move as slow as molasses in winter on the weekends.

The young, brash, loud Resident doctor lumbered through the door to see what was going on in response to the hospital page. He patted my daddy's hand. No response. He repeated, "Frank, Frank, FRANK," louder and louder, as if my father's hearing were the problem. No response. He patted my daddy's cheek to no response. His chubby hand dug in his white lab coat pocket and brought out a little flashlight with the Lilly pharmaceutical logo, exactly like the ones my father brought home over the years. He lifted my daddy's eyelid and shone the light onto the pupil. No response.

The lumbering, brash, loud Resident transformed into a serious, alarmed and lightning-fast Doctor, bellowing rapid-fire directions to nurses. I heard "MRI" and "stroke" and "not responsive." Mom and I holding hands, I began a silent prayer, powerless to do anything else.

Early that evening, the Saturday before Father's Day, my father lapsed into a coma. Almost 6 hours after watching my father contort and shudder the MRI confirmed what my mom and I already knew. My father had had a massive stroke.

Mom and I sat all night in the waiting room of ICU, hoping to be called by the nurses to come back and see for ourselves that daddy was still breathing. The problem was, he wasn't. He was intubated and placed on a ventilator. We kept hearing the word "complications" when we spoke to any medical staff. The next days and nights were a blur of sitting in the ICU waiting room listening to other families dealing with traumatic situations: nearly fatal car accidents on the narrow beach road, heart attacks, even an accidental poisoning. We watched as these families' loved ones got better and were moved to regular hospital rooms. My mom and I held hands when one family was called into the hallway for an update. We knew that was not a good sign, and it wasn't. We kept hoping and praying for Daddy, our loved one, to be moved to a regular hospital room.

Because the transplant surgeon was a med school buddy of my dad's, before the transplant they decided it would be best to fix the hernia on my father's left side and place the kidney there, avoiding a future hernia procedure. On paper, it all made sense. *On paper.* Off paper, they decided to go against the usual protocol of removing a transplant recipient's appendix and placing the donated kidney in that space. Off paper, in real life, my father's life hung in the balance

The night of my father's stroke, I became numb; I couldn't feel any part of my body or emotions. That night, some part of me knew the trauma was too much and that I couldn't emotionally afford to look at reality. The reason-based, logical part of my mind also shut down in order for me to survive the siege at hand.

Post coma, pneumonia lingered for weeks. Then torturous physical therapy ensued. Making progress, it was suggested my father go to a specialized rehab center. He was transferred in a poorly air-conditioned ambulance in the sweltering Texas heat of early September to a highly marketed rehab facility in Houston. We found out too late this facility actually had no way to care for his level of disability but loved his insurance policy. The nurse/ saleswoman stopped returning our phone calls. Rampant infections again engulfed Daddy's body. After a few weeks he stabilized and was transferred back to the hospital in Galveston where his long-time colleagues welcomed us back. Then pneumonia struck again. He got weaker and skinnier. He disappeared inside himself for days on end, non-responsive. His doctor told us not to get caught up in the daily ups and downs.

My father had always hated being sick, hated being a patient. He and his surgical partner used to joke, "If I'm living in ICU, bring me a gun." We half thought Joe might just bring that gun. After one particularly gloomy day in the hospital, I cried to the transplant doctor, "I thought giving him my kidney was such a good thing." He replied, "Honey, it was. Your kidney is the only thing keeping him alive right now."

And there it was. I was the reason my father, family and his friends were suffering.

The next months were a jumble of flights back and forth to L.A. where my so-called life existed; at least that was where my apartment, job and boyfriend were. When I was in L.A., all I could think about was my dad and feeling guilty that I wasn't in Galveston supporting my mom. I also felt errant that Frank, newly married, who lived twenty minutes from my childhood home was doing all the heavy lifting of taking care of that home while my father fought for his life in Galveston 100 miles away.

That psychic little voice that whispers things like "call home" whispered in my head before Thanksgiving that I should go in earlier than planned. I re-booked my flight (much easier to do in 1989 than today) and arrived to be with my father on what turned out to be his last good days. He shone his love of me in his half smile when I walked in the door, both our tears flowing. (One side of his body was completely paralyzed and could not move at all—hence the half smile.) I hugged him as tightly as I could.

The next day, his liver function plummeted and the kidney I gave Daddy began to fail. Returning to my father's room from the Ladies' room outside of the Surgical ICU where my father was, I smelled the oddest odor—apple pie baking. Surgical ICU was nowhere near the hospital cafeteria. I'd never smelled any food there other than the rogue bag of fast food someone brought in with them. I looked around as I walked through the hall—no pie. I looked at the nurse's station—no pie. I couldn't explain it.

My brother and sister-in-law brought a Thanksgiving feast to my mom and me in Galveston. They arrived on Wednesday evening, in time to visit with Daddy for a bit. After seeing my father Thursday morning, we went back to the condo to eat turkey, dressing and pie. Halfway through the meal, I noticed I couldn't taste anything. We went back to the hospital that afternoon before Frank and Lori left to go see her parents. (My God what we do to satisfy others during the holidays.)

Thanksgiving night, my father's monitors started beeping like he was flat lining. A nurse rushed in and lifted his left arm, which seemed to get his heart back in rhythm. After she left, I saw my unconscious, paralyzed father move his neck in such a way to try to pull out the IV tube.

My mom came in the room and I told her I was going to the chapel.

I kneeled as I had many times before—sometimes believing my prayers were heard and just as often, feeling like they were ignored. Those prior prayers had been filled with pleading, bargaining, promising and desperation for my father to get better, come home, live life in his zesty way.

That night I looked at the cross, got on the kneeling bench, bowed my head, closed my eyes and said a brand new prayer.

"I surrender. If he is ready to go, take him." My tears flowed hot as lava down my cheeks. "I don't want to be the reason he struggles to stay. I let go if he lets go." I pulled the unopened pocket pack of tissue from my purse and used every single one of them before getting up from the kneeling bench.

Very early the next morning, Friday, November 24, 1989, before we woke, the phone rang at the condo. My mom and I both knew that was not good. "Get over here fast, he's going," the nurse told my mom.

Before we could even throw on clothes and get out the door, the phone rang again. My father was gone.

On the way to the hospital, a flaming sunrise illuminated the clouds over the Gulf of Mexico creating one of those crowning halo effects where the rays of the sun stretch upward further than the eye can see. I mumbled to my mom that I'd always heard a sky that looked like that was a door opening to heaven. We both howled our grief.

My father's room was oddly quiet. I missed the hum of all the machines that were now turned off. All the tubes had been removed. He looked so peaceful. His hands were still warm though his face was losing color quickly. Mom and I were on either side of him and I saw her holding back her tears, for me.

I walked out to give her some alone time with my father, the love of her life. His room was right across from the nurse's station. I was hoping for a smile or a hug or something from one of the nurses that had become like family. They were all off for the holiday weekend so I did not get a hug or a smile or an acknowledgment. A nurse I'd never seen before erased my father's name from the white board and asked, "Can I help you?" when I froze right in front of the counter.

"Not anymore," I rasped, bursting into mournful wailing. "You just erased my daddy's name." The woman looked at me with confusion, then recognition, and finally, horror. I ran to the Ladies' room and locked the door, fully opening the sink faucets as I screamed at the top of my voice before vomiting.

CHAPTER 3

From One Body to Another

The day after my father's stroke and ensuing coma was Father's Day. In the early afternoon, we were allowed to see my father, one at a time. My mom went in first and when she came out, shaken to her core, I urged her to go get something to eat in the cafeteria. Neither of us had eaten for about twenty-four hours. I'm sure she got a coffee to go and went outside to smoke instead. It's what I would have done.

The nurse handed me a yellow gown and mask, asking if I had been sneezing, coughing or felt sick in any way. "No," I said, knowing the sickness in my heart didn't count.

I slipped into the gown and quickly wrapped the ties around my waist before tying them in front. I put on the mask with an odd familiarity as if I'd done it every day my whole life and entered my father's sealed and quarantined room in the ICU.

The mechanical whoosh of the ventilator was a little like the white noise a ceiling fan makes, oddly soothing. The oxygen tube was cool to the touch and green gunk slid down the NG (nasal-gastric) tube, pumping out infection from my father's abdominal cavity. The tubes were crooked and I adjusted them so they at least looked more comfortable.

I checked the IV bag level and the various tubes' entrance points like an RN. All looked to be in order. I picked up my father's swollen left hand and rested it on mine. I placed my right hand as softly and with as little pressure as possible on his left shoulder. I began a silent prayer, begging the infection raging like wildfire in my father's body to come into my strong and healthy body. "Dear God, please let me handle the infection so Daddy can get well and come home."

Right before my father died, I started getting sick.

First up was a simple urinary tract and bladder infection, which hurled the doctors into overdrive. Terrified the infection would spread to my remaining kidney they loaded me up on antibiotics. I'd feel better for a few weeks then wham, the infection would come back.

Pretty soon I was in a cycle of monthly bladder infections. In February 1990, a few months after my father's death, I was placed on a low-dose antibiotic for six months to slay the invader once and for all.

Also in February, the shock of my father's death began to lift, and I found myself wearing the mantle of failure. Daily, I had to shake off the desire to lie in bed and hide in shame. I imagined my aunts disappointed in me for not saving their little brother. My mom cried just about every time we spoke on the phone. My brother was dealing with his own grief and didn't know how to talk to me about any of it. My coworkers were strangely quiet around me. Some friends didn't know what to say and stopped calling. My harsh inner-judge convinced me I was a colossal failure. Most days I felt like I didn't deserve to use up oxygen. "See, all that pre-op glorification was bullshit," I told myself. And I was mad, rage-filled even. I had counted on the promise of my father living, and the amazing connection all the brochures on kidney transplants talked about. And I wanted, no, *needed* that healing—that magical healing and unlocking of horns.

I discovered that courage is not about doing something heroic sounding, like donating a kidney. Courage is a daily decision to get out of bed, go to work, remember to eat, and show up for life despite corrosive feelings of failure and the amount of pain in your heart. I learned that courage is a conscious choice to focus on other people. Maybe the most important discovery is that courage is to not always believe the inner-judge when it howls, "Failure! You're a failure! Why would you even try to (fill in the blank)?"

Heartbroken, I struggled through a numb haze to continue working for the party company and act as if everything was normal. The pretense was wearying. Every time I was around anyone who sneezed or coughed, I came down with pharyngitis. The antibiotic Erythromycin was added to the low-dose antibiotic I was taking for the bladder infection. The pharyngitis would go away for four to six weeks only to come back even stronger. More Erythromycin.

My stomach began to ache. I swung between constipation and diarrhea.

I kept asking the doctors, "What is wrong with me? Why aren't the drugs working? They've always worked. My body loves antibiotics." They couldn't explain it. I could see in some friends' eyes they thought I was making up some of my illness, as an excuse to not have to push myself to audition all the time or dig deeply in grief therapy. Of course, these were people who had not lost a parent. Or donated a body part to a beloved only to have them die anyway.

One afternoon in 1991, about eighteen months after my father's death, my mentor and acting coach, Maria Gobetti said, "I think you have what I had." We were talking in her theater where I had gone to get her advice on finding a new agent. "I think all those antibiotics are making you sicker," she said. Then she shared her experience of being "over-antibiotic-ed" as she called it. My symptoms certainly sounded like hers: exhausted no matter how much sleep and rest; stomach and bowel discomfort; inexplicable aches and pains; repetitive illness and taking of antibiotics, and worst of all, mental fog. I'd always prided myself on my mental sharpness and my mind felt like the dullest of dull knives.

Maria gave me the business card of a doctor in Santa Monica. She said he practiced alternative medicine, but was also an MD. His partners were also MDs and she thought all were good but preferred Dr. Allen.

I looked at the card every day, wondering what alternative meant. I'd begun reading *A Course in Miracles* earlier that year, and randomly flipped it open for inspiration. I read about coincidence and how there really isn't such a thing. I closed the book and wondered if that meant I should call the alternative doctor.

Two days later, I spiraled into another bout of pharyngitis and thought there was no way an alternative doctor could make me any worse, so I called to schedule an appointment. I was asked to do a pre-appointment interview questionnaire and mail it back. I played my best "I'm a surgeon's daughter" card and finally convinced the receptionist I needed to see the doctor immediately because I was so sick. She explained that their office worked with patients to stay well. What the hell? What kind of doctors are these I wondered?

Dr. Allen did not give me antibiotics, which I asked for. "Why not?" I asked, pining for Western medicine's quick fix. "Because they are the problem. Your immune system has weakened with each round of antibiotics you've been on." That day I was given my first IV drip of liquid vitamins and couldn't believe the rush of energy I experienced. I tingled from the inside—not too far from an orgasmic tingle. I was sent home with Echinacea and other herbs that tasted so bad I was sure they had to be good for me. I gargled with hydrogen peroxide every two hours as prescribed and threw away all the cherry lozenges I was in the habit of sucking on. I used natural sea salt spray instead of my favored Afrin. A week later my throat didn't hurt and my fever was gone, but I still felt like crap.

When I told my mom I'd gone to a different doctor and not been given antibiotics she erupted, "Mary Catherine," (when she used my full name, she meant business), "What are you thinking? I thought you said these are real doctors, *MDs*."

"They are, Mom. They just think the body is meant to heal itself with proper support." I pretended to believe it, parroting what the doctor had told me.

"That sounds like a bunch of California hooey. Please go see your ENT."

"There's no reason to, Mom. My sore throat is gone and so is my fever."

Once out of the acute illness, I had to answer the lengthy questionnaire and go through a series of tests that were different from any medical tests I'd ever done before. They examined my hair strands under a microscope. I had to bring them three days' worth of poop. (Rich, my live-in boyfriend, was definitely *not* down with the fact that I stored my poop in a baggie in the refrigerator. I placed the baggie in a brown paper sack so neither of us had to look at it.) After all was analyzed it was determined I had "Systemic Candidiasis," commonly referred to as Candida.

"You have no nutritional values in your cells, hair, excrement or blood."

"Huh?" I sputtered, staring at Dr. Allen.

He told me to read *The Yeast Syndrome,* and when I did, I saw I had *every* symptom of Candida. I could not believe what I was reading. The very thing I was raised to believe in, Western medicine, was making me sick. Everything I loved to eat and drink (bread, beer, pizza, *any* dessert) was making me sicker.

My mom freaked out about what I was reading and doing. She thought the whole thing was crazy and didn't hold back in telling me so.

Over the next six months, I followed the Candida cleanse eating plan meticulously. The first three days I felt great. My stomach bloat started shrinking and my stomach stopped aching all the time. Lulled into a false sense of wellbeing, I thought I wasn't going to experience any of the "die-off" symptoms the book listed.

Day four I woke and didn't know whether I needed to sit on the toilet seat or hang my head over the edge. I sat and put the garbage can by my feet. Day five I could hardly get out of bed. I felt bruised on the inside and could not stand up

36

straight my stomach cramped so badly. Day six a three-day headache kicked in.

Tortured by watching me writhe and slither around in pain, Rich begged me to go see a regular doctor. I didn't. I just kept making my own salad dressing and cornbread and drank unsweetened coffee.

The intensity halted as suddenly as it started. All the while, I drove the twenty-six miles from Burbank to the doctor's office in Santa Monica for those hour-long infusions of tingle-inducing IV Vitamin Drips.

I stopped running and exercising because the alternative doctor said I needed to let my body rest. I took the herbs he told me to take. I carried my baggie of supplements everywhere I went.

I wrote in my journal nearly every day during the process, finished re-reading *A Course in Miracles* yet was plagued with the omnipresent question: Was I somehow disavowing my father by taking this alternative route?

My mind and emotions detoxed right along with my body. I went days without feeling like an utter failure. After the intensity of the Candida die-off lifted, I had an a-ha moment. I remembered the day I sat at my father's ICU bedside and invited his infection into my strong and healthy body. Rather than the short visit I had intended, the infection and illness had moved in, painted the walls and rearranged the damn furniture.

During the third stage of the anti-Candida eating plan, I traveled to my hometown, Port Arthur, for a family event. Shopping in a local store, the clerk looked at the name on my credit card. She looked up at me smiling and asked, "Are you related to Dr. Williford?"

THE OVARIAN CHRONICLES

I smiled back and said, "Yes, I am his daughter."

"Well honey, your daddy is an angel. He saved my mother's life. Other doctors told her there was nothing that could be done. Your daddy cut out that growth and she's still here twenty years later!"

I left the store quickly and ducked into my dad's Jag. "Daddy, oh Daddy, why did you have to go?" I sobbed, curled up on my right side, my fingers pawing at the smooth leather of the seat. The ache of missing him flooded my body, yet I felt oddly connected to him and comforted by sitting in the cocoon-like driver's seat of his car. My mom was working herself up to sell it, and I was very grateful she hadn't yet.

Lingering over breakfast at my mom's the next morning, looking out the bay window at my father's backyard green-house, I finally found the courage to ask, "Do you blame me for daddy dying?"

She burst into tears and asked, "Are you mad? Of course I don't blame you. You did the most amazing thing any of us could do." I started to cry. She got up and pulled me to my feet so she could hug me.

Stroking my head, she said, "He didn't die because of your kidney. He died from stroke complications. Or appendicitis complications that led to the stroke complications." She backed away, lifted my chin and looked intently into my eyes. "Honey, *none* of us blame you. Please don't think that. Please, please, please don't think that." Then she squeezed me tighter and tighter.

"As grief-filled as we all are, I've told everyone we have no idea what you must be going through. You have the added burden of being the donor."

That day, the taunting inner voice that relentlessly chanted, "You're a failure, why would you even try to (fill in the blank)," eased up infinitesimally.

All these years later, I still follow the basic anti-Candida meal plan. Do I miss beer and bread and pizza? Of course I do. And I miss cake and ice cream, too. But I love having the energy to run, dance, play and, in my work as a life coach, support others on their journeys to self-love, forgiveness and fulfillment.

As I sat in my car having just learned from Dr. K about the suspect growth on my ovary, I knew that whatever happened, I would have to summon all that I had learned from 1991 to 2010, about walking the fine line between Western medicine and holistic health. I would have to listen to my body. What I couldn't have known then, but I was to learn, I was also going to have to finally learn to open myself up to love. More specifically, open myself up to receive love. I was already really good at giving it. Oh, the learning. Oh, the healing.

CHAPTER 4

Shatterings

When I was twenty-six, the year after my father died, I gave my heart and soul to a man named Rich. The man who in our seventeenth year together, with one glance, could make me feel like I'd just fallen in love with him; make me forget my own dreams and swoon into the comfortable familiarity of his perfect arms. I. Loved. This. Man.

It was the fall of 1990 and I lied on the application to get my first waitressing job at the about-to-open-hotspot billiard hall and fancy restaurant, The Hollywood Athletic Club, helmed by an up and coming L.A. chef. The name of the restaurant/ billiard hall was taken from the actual name and history of the location. The building was constructed in the 1920's and was a social gathering spot as well as the go-to place to get in shape for the likes of Errol Flynn, Mary Pickford, John Wayne, swimming goddess Esther Williams, Humphrey Bogart and Clark Gable. I loved that history! The lie? I said I'd been a cocktail waitress at some of my favorite watering holes that had gone out of business. I'd never worked in a restaurant or bar, though the catering gigs I listed were true. Tom, the British owner looked me up one side and down the other like most casting directors did. It was clear my looks mattered more than where, or even if, I'd served cocktails.

The invitation-only, non-public opening night was memorable because I proved to myself I could do math in my head (and on a napkin) well enough to be a cocktail waitress. It was memorable because I felt like I was earning some sort of B.S. actor's stripe.

Most of all, that early October night was unforgettable because that evening, I met Rich, a friend of the owner.

I carved my way through the enormous two rooms of pool tables, making sure to pass by the one he and his two buddies were playing on every time I could. Bent over the corner of the pool table to make his next shot, I noticed his perfect blue jeans butt. "Get a grip," I told myself.

His buddies got more flirtatious with each large Sapporo beer. One said, "Hey, I write love songs for a living. Want to hear one?" I started laughing and held up my hand. "No thanks—I'm more into Gloria Gaynor's "I Will Survive" right now! I just had a bad breakup complete with Chinese food dripping from the ceiling." The other tried to get me to take a Jägermeister shot with them, assuring me that was the best way through heartache. Rich, who was not keeping pace with their consumption scolded them, "Hey, we aren't her only customers. Stop trying to make her drink with you." Turning to me, he said, "I'm sorry—they don't get out of the studio much!"

I was used to his buddies' style of drunken flirting and said so. "I bet you are," he said, smiling.

"I hope you are driving!" I said after the check was settled.

"Always with this crew of hooligans," he said, winking one of his lake blue eyes and flashing a smile that made me tingle. I imagined running my fingers through his long sun-streaked hair. Instead, I smiled my best inviting smile, winked back and cheered, "Good luck!" as he swung his leather jacket over his shoulder and herded his buddies in the direction of the front door.

I almost dropped the AMEX branded leatherette check folder on seeing fifty dollars in bills, my tip on a check of $100.00. I might just like waitressing after all, I thought.

It was another two weeks before I saw Rich again, sans hooligan buddies. He was shooting pool with the owner Tom in the middle of the afternoon. I walked by and said, "Hello!"

The ever-flirtatious Tom, thinking I was saying hello to him, introduced me to Rich.

Rich replied, "We met the night of your opening party. She is awesome!" He leaned over the corner of the table to make a shot. The urge to run my hand through his hair overcame me again.

Tom said, "Glad to hear it." The sound of the ball slamming into the opposite corner pocket provoked a "Bugger!" from him, then another "Glad to hear it."

I was there for an employee training on the wine list so was a little startled when the owner asked me to bring them two bottles of Pellegrino water.

"With lime, please," said Rich.

"I remembered that," I smiled at him, feeling the flush of a blush rise up on my cheeks.

Turning toward the bar to fetch their water, I caught a glimpse of Rich's crimson flush in the enormous wall mirror.

"Wanna go for a drink?" Rich asked, whisper-quiet when I set down his Pellegrino water and a shot glass of extra lime wedges.

"Sure, the meeting is over at five," I whispered back.

I do not remember one thing said during the training by the wine distributor's sommelier. I couldn't stop thinking about Rich's long blonde hair. I couldn't stop thinking about his cowboy boots with the very cool silver concha embellishment on the left one. I couldn't stop thinking about the way my stomach flip-flopped when he smiled at me. And I didn't want to stop thinking about those things.

Settling into a booth at the Cat & Fiddle pub across Sunset Boulevard from The Hollywood Athletic Club, I started laughing. Rich's left eyebrow went up.

"Isn't it funny to leave one bar and walk across the street to another?" I asked, still laughing.

"More private here," he said before taking a swig of his Sapporo beer.

"I have a habit of peeling labels off of beer bottles," I said, making a show of sitting on my hands so I couldn't peel off the label on my Amstel Light bottle.

"How are you going to drink it," Rich asked with a sly grin.

Laughing at myself I demonstrated by leaning to the right, lifting my left butt cheek and slowly raising my left hand up to the dark amber bottle. I took a swig before lowering my hand to the seat and re-sitting on my hand. He looked at me, shaking his head but smiling that smile that made my insides hot.

"How do you know Tom?" I asked.

"I'm doing some work in the music studio above the club. Hey, my friend Gene, uh, the one who writes love songs, was quite taken with you the other night! He thinks he kind of blew it though since he was a bit drunk. Anyway, would you be interested in going out with him?"

"I'd rather go out with you," I blurted before I could stop myself. Both of us had wide-open eyes and raised eyebrows. "I mean, I'm sorry, your friend is nice and all, but . . . ."

"Wow. I'm . . . really . . . flattered. But . . . well . . . I have this obligation . . . ."

"Holy shit—you're married?" I asked, quickly looking at his naked left ring finger.

"No . . ."

"Your mother is dying?" I fished.

"No, God no. It's just, I'm engaged to a girl back home."

"Let me just say—any guy that says he has an obligation to marry me isn't somebody I want to marry," I said, unable to halt the disappointment tinged explosion from deep inside me.

Where on earth did that come from, I wondered. Rich leaned back in the booth, nodded his head a few times then started laughing and said, "That's great! We're gonna get along just fine!"

My mind raced ahead with his words. "Gonna get along just fine . . . what does that mean?"

"I don't know," he said softly, almost to himself.

I noticed the nail of my right index finger swiping at the moist label.

Clearly ready for a change of subject, he asked, "Would you like to see my new recording studio? It's just across the hill in the valley."

"Mm-hmm," I said, swigging the last drop of my beer.

What it turned out to mean is we fell into a routine for about six weeks. He'd swing by the pool hall on Saturday night about an hour before closing; order a basket of fries and a bottle of Pellegrino. After I closed out, we'd go eat a late-night breakfast at Danny's Hollywood Diner or Canter's Deli. We talked about everything under the sun including the fact that both of our fathers died when we were each twenty-five, and about our love for the same music by 70's bands Supertramp and Fleetwood Mac, to Frank Sinatra, big bands and brass bands. He shared how he felt backed into a corner by his fiancé to get married even though he'd always had his doubts about the relationship. I shared how my last relationship ended because it was clear the guy had no respect for my desired career. He had constantly belittled my rehearsal time when it interfered with something he wanted to do. Rich nodded his understanding.

By late October, two weeks into our little routine I knew I was in trouble—the falling-in-love-with-an-unavailable-man kind of trouble. I thought he might be in trouble, too. When he took me back to my car outside The Hollywood Athletic Club after one of our wee morning hours breakfast and conversation "dates," I couldn't curtail the urge in time and kissed him square on the mouth.

We rocked back from each other, both taken by surprise. I hurriedly said, "See you later," and got into my car as fast as I could, bursting into tears as I sped away. How could I be so stupid to fall in love with a man who was upfront about being engaged to another woman? I'm not "the other woman" type. Am I? I wondered. No, definitely not. I'm selfish and like all the attention.

I don't share my toys when it comes to love. And I don't screw a sister, even a sister I don't know.

Mid-November, a month later, standing side by side on the observation deck of the famed Griffith Park Observatory, heads tilted up taking in a beautiful clear sky, he reached for my hand. I felt the heat of my tears.

"I'm falling in love with you and won't be your last fling, or your excuse not to marry her. You need to figure out what you are doing," I said, taking my hand back.

"You're right," he said quietly as I strained to hear him above the wind and conversation of lovers strolling on the walkway behind us. "Can we be friends?" He asked so earnestly that I reached for his hand.

"Yes," I said, not able to imagine my life without the feeling I got from his smile.

The week of Thanksgiving he phoned and asked, "How about I swing by, and we go for a bike ride Friday afternoon on Venice Beach boardwalk? The last thing you need to do is mope around all day." I had shared over one of our late night/early morning breakfasts that my father had died the Friday morning after Thanksgiving, and here he was offering to relieve some of my grief on that first anniversary.

"I'd like that," I said, even though I don't really enjoy bike riding.

In mid-December, we decided on no contact before he returned to Canada for Christmas. Before I left to visit my family, I re-read the holiday card he gave me dozens of times, looking for a clue. What was he going to do? He wrote he'd never met a woman like me, and that I challenged him as a person more than anyone he knew. Was that a good thing? I wasn't sure. But

I really loved that I did challenge him, for whatever reason. I was certainly challenging myself to not sway his decision.

He dissolved the engagement. As soon as he arrived his fiancé knew something was up and confronted him. He returned to L.A. in January, devastated by the pain he had caused in dissolving the engagement. In spite of his saying he was not ready to enter a serious relationship and that he didn't think marriage was for him, on March 1, 1991, we moved into an apartment together in Burbank, close to his music studio and my theatre home base. I knew if he had walked the path toward marriage before, he was likely to walk it again.

I fell more deeply in love as his passion and creativity roused me to be more intentional with my own. His vision for what the business of music and art could be, what the world could be, inspires me as much today as it did the first time he shared his ideas with me in October of 1990. I had fun helping him run his music studio in between my own rehearsals, performing in plays, and auditioning. I quit working as a cocktail waitress when the once upscale clientele morphed into a rowdy crowd (as in grabbing my butt, and on the night I quit mid-shift, my left breast) and returned to working part time at the party company. Rich and I pursued our dreams individually and collectively. And let's just say we had each other's number physically. Our connection on all levels was a potent passion cocktail.

Just over a year after moving in together, Rich and I decided to get married. We shared the news with our moms.

Mine asked, "Are you pregnant? This seems so sudden."

"No, there are other reasons to get married," I roared at her, trying to ignore my own concerns.

Rich and I flew up to Mammoth, CA to look at possible wedding sites. He was also checking out different properties to use as location recording studios. Over a steak and lobster dinner, I began sobbing. The real reason we were talking about marriage was due to the slowness in receiving his business owner visa. Several of his Canadian friends were concerned as tales of deportation grew. The idea of INS appearing at my door and dragging Rich away was just too upsetting . . . until that dinner.

I struggled to get my words out between sobs. "Rich, I love you with all my heart. But I can't do this. I don't want to get married out of fear of the INS. This is not how I've imagined getting married. It feels like a shotgun deal. I want us to marry out of love and passion, not because of some perceived threat." If we hadn't been in a public place, I would have been howling my sobs instead of trying to quiet them. I knew I wanted to be with him forever, but not like this.

The look of relief mixed with pensive sadness on his face told me he was thinking along the same lines.

He offered his hands to me across the table; his blue eyes that made me melt beamed love and strength into me. After regaining a little composure, I placed my hands in his.

"I agree. I don't want you to feel obligated to marry me. I don't ever want to do that to anybody, especially you." Here we were back at obligation and marriage.

A week later, my period was overdue. I called my doctor, and he said since I'd changed to another version of the Pill a few months back hoping to find one that didn't trigger migraine headaches, it was not uncommon to skip a period or experience breakthrough bleeding. I took an EPT home test anyway—

negative. My period didn't start the next month. I scheduled an appointment with my doctor and that blood test for pregnancy was negative. Next, he performed a vaginal ultrasound. His puzzled expression worried me. Then he said, "Well, we now know why your period isn't starting. You *are* pregnant."

My doctor couldn't explain to me why all the tests were negative. He couldn't explain why the Pill hadn't worked. He couldn't explain why he hadn't caught that I was pregnant before inserting the ultrasound wand. He couldn't explain what my continuing to take the Pill would mean to the health of the fetus. He couldn't explain why, even when asked for the fifth time, all the pregnancy tests, including blood, had come back negative. He didn't know if the Candida was a factor. He rolled toward me on his low stool shaking his head ever so slightly, almost apologetically from side to side and uttered quietly, "This fetus may not be developing correctly. The blood test should have picked up the pregnancy." He paused, "You have a choice to make."

Rich left the choice to me, saying it was my body and that while being a parent was not in his plan at the moment, he was going to be there no matter what I chose.

It seemed ironic that we'd just decided to *not* get married and just over a month later discovered I was pregnant. If it was a joke, I wasn't laughing. I'd recently heard from a friend who'd been very sick and on a medication before she knew she was pregnant, and had just discovered her child was not going to develop mentally, physically or emotionally past toddler stage. I'd been on a stop-it-in-its-tracks drug for severe food poisoning (bacon wrapped shrimp on a steam table—just say no) in the first weeks of my unknown pregnancy, along with the Pill. Rich and I were not married, had no financial reserves, and I didn't know if we were going to make it, having just decided to delay marriage. I sat quietly at the foot of our bed swathed in my summer robe just out of the shower my hair dripping down my back, hands resting on my belly. Even though I cleared my mind, opened my heart and asked my body to speak to me, I did not feel that "presence" in me that many of my friends said they felt before they officially knew they were, indeed, pregnant. Next, I searched my reflection in the bathroom mirror for that "glow" pregnant women exude. It wasn't there. I looked pale instead. I didn't have morning sickness and didn't feel exhausted, the two key things my girlfriends reported during their pregnancies.

Before making my final decision, I pulled out a LIFE magazine I'd kept out of fascination and made myself re-read the article on embryonic stages. I re-read it and read it again. I knew I wanted children . . . in the future. I decided my youth and hard-won health were on my side. I ended the pregnancy.

After we decided not to marry but before we found out I was pregnant, Rich picked me up from the airport after a trip to visit my mom. He asked me how I felt about dogs to which I replied, "I love dogs! Why?" Grinning from ear to ear he said he had a surprise for me. I walked through the door of our apartment and dropped to the floor with delight as a five-month old golden retriever ran toward us. The dog's people were friends of a friend, and they had to move back to NYC suddenly and couldn't take their dog with them. We gladly took him in and his name became Chaub (a rhyme of his original name . . . Jobs).

Rich and I dove back into life. We also poured our hearts and souls into our growing and attention-consuming new "baby" puppy. We both had the ability to compartmentalize and managed to keep it together by day. At night, when I grieved, he held me tenderly, and through my tears did his own share of grieving. To this day, I don't exactly regret the decision I made. I am angry that I was in the 1% of users who get pregnant while on the Pill and that I had to make a decision at all. Every February, I think about how old that child would be.

Rich, ever the romantic and provider of fun, helped me live in the moment and appreciate more deeply the way a sunset colors the sky and the smell of rain. We snuggled in front of fireplaces and fire pits, in bar banquets, and on our sofa at home. We probably looked like we were on our honeymoon years into our relationship. We shone a little more in each other's presence than on our own. He brought coffee to wake me nearly every morning. I felt physically safe and had the feeling that he would stop the proverbial speeding bullet or bus if one were headed my way. Rich introduced me to the joys of science breakthroughs like nanotechnology and watching the NASA channel's footage that made me feel like I was floating through space from the perspective of shuttle missions. It was as calming as I found the meditation techniques that I shared with him, and let's just say he humored my Astrology shares! When we hugged, we fit.

When I turned thirty-three, after five years of living that good life with Rich, Chaub, and our second rescue dog, Sienna, (a golden retriever/chow mix) I felt anxious. I'd continued to support Rich in his business just as he supported my shift from acting to becoming a Life Coach. I felt ready for marriage and what we'd put off. I knew I wasn't twenty-something anymore and many of my friends had kids who were already in grade school. I felt left behind. When a baby smiled at me in a store, or when I saw a moving birth or parenting scene in a movie, or when I had a particularly rough second day of my period, longing overtook me and the Fairytale Fine mask that had me ignore little concerns like I was now in my thirties would shatter and clatter to the floor. "Can't you see how amazing our kids would be? How smart, beautiful, delightful, precious and loved they would be?"

Rich's normally open and kind face would screw itself into its own mask of "tough and gruff" as if to shield himself from the hurt he was causing me. He said he didn't really know if he wanted children, and certainly not now, as I increasingly did. As I sobbed, he'd say he would rather walk away than continue to cause me pain. That's when his tears flowed. "I can't bear to see you in such pain, Cat. You deserve better than me. I love you so much and want you to be happy." His tears gave me hope. And my Fairytale Fine mask grew thicker and thicker and morphed into the Suck It Up Buttercup mask that silenced my body's knowing.

Competing with my desire to start a family was the sense of failure that continued to lurk in the background after my father died with my kidney in him—the one that was supposed to save his life. I doubted my own deservingness to have children. Clearly, I was the problem, right? I also experienced debilitating migraines for days on end and asked myself, many times, how on earth could I take care of a child while lying in bed as still as possible for hours on end? Rich's arguments that we weren't ready financially, emotionally, or even physically to be parents became part of a wicked internal litany of "broken" and "failure" and "why bother?" I'd already failed at saving my daddy's life and at a certain point, Rich's dreams started floundering. It was all too easy for us to imagine failing as parents.

When I imagined walking away from our life, the refrain to "Midnight Train to Georgia" would play in my head, "I'd rather live with him in his world, than live without him in mine . . ."

And it was the truth. For. Years.

Until it wasn't. Until I couldn't ignore that I wasn't twenty-six, thirty-three or thirty-eight anymore. Until at forty-one the screaming urgency of my body and soul kept me up at night. Until no matter how madly I loved him or how much I believed in him or how much I'd invested in him, my desire for a baby was greater still.

Just out from under the burden of a three-acre lakefront estate property used as a recording studio and playground for never-grown-up-young-men, we experienced the simplicity of a two-bedroom beach condo and had a cushion of cash in the bank. It felt like a renewal into simplicity after years of complicated. I begged him to sit in the stillness and let this be "our" time rather than trying to change the world all the time.

"You're right, Cat. I'm so tired. But I just need to get back to why I love music." Restless to reclaim his dream, he couldn't sit in the stillness. Then he heard a recording studio was for sale—not just any studio, but the studio where his journey into the music business began. He asked if we could put our cushion of cash into escrow, to secure the studio while he found the right investor to partner with him. We were both still grieving—the loss of his grandfather, the loss of my grandmother, the loss of our beloved fur-babies, Chaub and Sienna. Seeing something light up his eyes again made me say yes. We went to the bank and initiated the draft. He said the deal would double or triple our cash cushion. I fell under the spell of his dream again. "If you help him get his, you'll get yours," whispered the Suck It Up Buttercup mask.

Rich took a music gig in Canada, to be closer to the studio in escrow . . . and to feel productive. This gave me time alone to realize what I'd done. Again. When I visited him, I saw that the music gig and the hope of that studio had done him some good. He was still tired, but energized in a way that got me excited about the future. Yet I really couldn't see me in this scenario. "Yes, I can work from anywhere via phone and Internet connection, but moving to Canada? Where does this leave my dream?" I asked him. Though I lived in CA and my mom was still in Texas and my brother in New Orleans, I couldn't imagine having to go through customs to visit them, or them me. Not long after I returned to L.A., Rich told me in a defeated tone one late night on the phone, the right investor did not materialize and the use-it-or-lose-it date of the escrow lapsed, taking our cash cushion with it.

At that moment, though dazed, I knew I could not suck it up one more time, delaying my dream for his. I had to make a stand for me, for us, for our future, or I'd regret it for the rest of my life. I had to rip off that Suck It Up Buttercup mask and break my silence once and for all. If I didn't, I knew I would become a very ugly, resentful version of myself. I had seen what that kind of resentment had done to many of my friend's relationships via divorce proceedings. All the spiritual and personal development I'd gone through would be for naught if I didn't make my stand.

I was introduced to a man named Scott right around this time, and we connected over politics. In our phone conversations, he would say things like: How has this guy not married you and given you everything you want? It was clear to me he had amorous feelings for me, and I wondered why I continued to talk with him. I could feel the fire I was playing with was as dangerous as it was emboldening me to make my stand.

And so, shaky, scared and biology-driven, I took a stand the next time I traveled to visit Rich.

I didn't stop when I saw his tears or when his usual arguments fell short of my desire. I turned statue stony when he said he was scared of losing me, hurting me, or turning into his father. Even when his arguments made sense, I stood strong. I could no longer ignore the urgency of my body's longing or the fire of my own dream. He asked if there was someone else. I said no. This was about what I wanted, what I deserved.

And that was when my slippery slope began. I knew Scott had said what I wanted to hear, and I also felt the sincerity of his words. Just like I didn't want to be Rich's reason for breaking it off with the woman he was engaged to when we met, Scott didn't want to be my reason to end it with Rich. But there was definitely adoring interest coming from Scott, and it somehow fortified me further.

Rich returned to our condo late spring. During the summer of our unwinding, we didn't imbibe. We didn't want to say and feel things fueled by alcohol. We tried to make love and it was as if my body closed up and wouldn't let him in. I developed a very "rare" vaginal infection. The more I tried to deny what was happening, the louder my body screamed at me. I wondered: Was it telling me to continue on our path to dissolution or to make a U-turn and forget that my heart and arms ached for my baby more than they ached to be in his embrace?

Two and a half months and a twenty-pound weight loss between us later, he said a final and exhausted, "No." Not the usual, "No, not now," but *"No,"* with a period after it.

Rich left. Well, technically I departed first for a planned trip we were both supposed to take to visit my mom and attend a high school reunion. He moved out that weekend instead. I was so hollow I felt like a paper doll.

When I walked in the backdoor of my mother's house, I could see in her eyes that I looked like hell. My brother was there too, and I saw in his eyes the knowing look of divorce devastation. Though Rich and I never married, our relationship outlasted many of our friend's marriages. That night, trying to find comfort in my childhood bed with its tall and hand-carved headboard, the bed my great-great grandfather had made for his bride, I'd never felt like more of a failure.

CHAPTER 5

Semi-Automatic Pilot

Schedules are glorious, convenient, inconvenient, reliable, protective, and brilliantly distracting, sometimes all at the same time. I decided to keep my day's planned schedule after leaving Dr. K's office, mostly because I didn't know what else to do.

When I walked in the door of my dermatologist's office an hour later, despite my soothing conversation with Veronica, my mind was on high alert. I stared at the waiting room's pink wallpaper, hoping to find meaning in the floral pattern, tuning out the derma-something-or-other infomercial on the CCTV and the gossipy conversations going on around me. My phone's ring promised someone's voice I wanted to hear. It was Scott, my current love, calling back. "Hello, hold on," I said, grabbing my bag and stepping into the hallway to talk.

I shared my news and his trademark glib factor evaporated. I felt his worry in the valley-girl upward inflection of the last word of his sentence, "I'm sure everything will be fine . . .

"I'm not dying for chrissake," I barked. Why did I sound so angry? And why was I taking it out on him?

"I know," he said, like a scolded dog ready to scurry away to avoid the pain of being hit.

Flooded by my real terror, I whispered, "But I'm . . . I'm terrified my dream of . . . of, *our* dream of . . . you know, is . . ." I couldn't even say it.

"I know, I know," he said on top of my words, not wanting me to have to speak the words out loud.

"I'd rather have you healthy and whole than no you and ten children," he said softly. We both took a deep breath. "Life is very strange," he said, sounding a million miles away, as he likely tried to find a way to "fix" what was happening to him, to me, to us.

One short week after we'd talked about getting married, while Rich and I were in the death throes of our relationship, Scott showed me a house he wanted to buy for us, to see if I could see myself living there. An excited yes was my answer! The next week, Scott almost died.

When we met, Scott had been in a one-year on and off again romance, though he said it was nothing like my almost two decades with Rich. There were complications there, too. She had needed a place to live (her prior roommate moved out suddenly and she couldn't afford to take over the apartment's rent) so while Scott was on location in Bermuda as Line Producer on a TV production, he sublet his second bedroom to her. He quit that gig two months into it due to a tyrannical producer. I was thrilled he was coming home early! But when he got home, she still had time on her sublet.

"You have got to be kidding me," I sulked the night he told me she was still there.

"I told her we are just friends, which is not that different from what we ever were. She and I have never been like you and Rich. She and I have never had that level of intimacy or commitment. But she was away on a film when you and I fell in love and I don't want to hurt her—she's not in a good place." I usually loved that Scott fought for the underdog and helped anyone in need, but I didn't love his charitable stand on this issue. Of course, I had no firm ground to stand on. Some of Rich's clothes still hung on "his" side of the closet and mementos of our life together lingered on walls and shelves.

Scott and I had not shared our wanna-be relationship with many people yet, most especially our in-limbo loves, but we talked about how we would be a for real, *we,* once past the extricating limbo. "What are you doing, Cat?" I'd ask my reflection. "How can you love two men like this? How can you talk forever and want babies with both of them?" I had no answer to what was happening. I looked for signs as I ran on the beach, collecting whole sand dollars, pausing to look at the patterns the broken ones made. I asked the dolphin who swam parallel to the shore for advice as I ran. I used multiple divination tools like tarot cards and rune stones to understand my feelings and mental state. I felt compelled by something inside me that I'd never experienced before. I also felt like my brain was broken somehow as I couldn't make sense of it all.

I was out of town the weekend that Scott's insides exploded. When I called him on Sunday to tell him what time to pick me up at the airport on Monday so we could see each other for a bit before I got on yet another airplane on Wednesday, I got his voicemail. We'd gotten in the habit of not leaving messages, relying instead on the "missed call" caller I.D. feature. When he called back, I answered with my customary "Heeeyyy," infused with a sexy drawl.

Instead of Scott's usual "Hey gorgeous!" I heard a woman's voice. "Did you call Scott?" My heart squeezed tight. Even though rapid-fire thoughts flew through my mind, I answered calmly.

"Um, yes, I did. Who is this?" I asked, already knowing, and making up another zillion stories in my mind, none of them good, about why she was calling me back on his phone.

"This is Karen. Scott is in hospital."

"Oh my God! Did he have a heart attack?" I blurted. I'd been lounging in my hotel's fluffy bathrobe and I jumped up, as if being at full attention would change something. Scott had been under so much pressure at his new production job. He was also moon-lighting as an ad-hoc contractor foreman on a friend's home renovation that wasn't going well, so a heart attack was the only reason I could think of why this virile, healthy, rock-climbing, former-swim-champion, athletic man would be in the hospital. The night before I left, he'd looked so stressed out I'd even said to him, "You need to say no to some of these people. You are going to have a flipping heart attack."

She tried to explain to me what happened and I heard "choked" "bleeding" "vomiting blood" and that Scott was on death's door with collapsing lungs when the head of Gastroenterology at UCLA performed a life-saving surgery.

The next day I landed at the Burbank airport, took a cab to my car at Veronica's in nearby Studio City and drove immediately across town to the hospital in Santa Monica. My insides twisted, and I felt nauseous.

Rounding the hospital hallway corner, I saw her for the first time, talking on the phone outside his door. She was the opposite of me: olive skin, dark hair, waif-thin, makeup-less. Dark shadows circled her eyes and she looked wired from too much caffeine. OK, that wired from too much caffeine look we shared. She motioned to me to wait a moment. I obliged. When she finished her call, I said flatly, "I'm Cat, we spoke last night." No fanfare. She filled me in on what was happening medically. Various family members, she said, were flying in and she had to leave for the airport soon to pick them up. I told her I would sit with Scott so she could go to the cafeteria and get a cup of tea, suggesting in my sweetest advice-giver voice, "You must take care of yourself as you take care of others." I wasn't really all that concerned for her. I wanted to be alone with Scott.

When another call came in, she left, and I stood in the doorway to Scott's room, flashing back to when I first saw my father in the ICU. I froze. The robust man of a week before, tanned, strong, in charge, looked fragile and slight in spite of being six-foot tall. I'd never noticed how skinny his calves were. As I looked at him dozing, pillows propping up his upper body and head, the IVs, the NG tube snaking out of his nose, his ghostly paleness and helplessness kicked me into "nurse" mode.

My tours-of-duty in hospitals have instilled a nurse's checklist in my head. I examined Scott's IVs and noticed one had blown because his left hand was twice its normal size. I noted the urine bag level was okay. I was checking the blood pressure and heart rate screen when he slowly opened his eyes half-mast. I leaned in to kiss his forehead and startled him, and just for a brief moment he looked as if he didn't know who I was. I started to cry softly. He blinked, looked around to see if Karen was still there and I said, "I sent her to the cafeteria."

Though weak and more than a little drugged he looked at me with intent pleading eyes and whispered, "Please, please, please, no drama. I can't take it right now."

Panic whirled inside me as the always-panicky eight-year old within, terrified of abandonment, felt pushed away. I took a deep breath and then another. This wasn't abandonment. We'd talked about how much I, he, we did not want to hurt people. This was survival kicking in. He knew I was leaving again; he knew Rich was coming back into town, and he knew he needed help.

Semi-calm returned, I nodded my head and said soothingly, "No drama. Promise." Drama was the last thing either of us wanted or needed.

"I'm here for you, whatever you need, Scott. I don't have to leave again."

"Keep your plans. My mom and aunts are here, and I will have plenty of help. Now is not the time to meet them all," he said, falling back into a doze.

I sat on the edge of the chair, holding his hand, loving him and praying. I couldn't help imagining if the scenario was reversed. I thought about what I felt like after the kidney transplant. I had needed simple and instead went through the exhausting hoopla of family birthday celebrations. It all seemed crazy in hindsight. No, I didn't want to force anything, in particular an ultimatum. And really, I had no right to as Rich was coming to town in a few weeks. "What are you doing?" I asked myself again.

The way my insides lurched, I knew that life had just taken a severe swing, not unlike when I was eight and daddy collapsed or later, when he was dying after the kidney transplant. At least I knew not to ask Scott's infection to come into my healthy body.

When Karen came back from the cafeteria, I made my exit. She followed me into the hall and asked if I worked with Scott. I felt her suspicion. As lightly as I could, and mustering a little laugh, I replied, "No, we connected over politics and haven't stopped debating since." We had spirited debates and shared with each other our experiences in the trenches. I reiterated the importance of taking care of her own wellbeing, telling her I'd been in her shoes. When I left, I heard my backless shoe heels echo a rhythmic beat down the hospital corridor.

Because Rich was coming to town, and because Karen was still subletting the second bedroom, she took care of Scott when he first got home and continued to do so for three months before making her departure. My spiritual mentor told me it was good I couldn't swoop in and save the day as saving and rescuing others was a pattern I was trying to break. "Let him come to you, darling. No chasing." Besides, I was still trying to rescue my dream.

Scott was unable to do much of anything. The surgeon had removed his spleen and re-arranged his innards, placing his stomach up into his chest. His entire digestive system needed to reboot and learn how to work again. He slept most of the day and was awake at night, making it hard to find a time when we were both awake enough to talk. When we did, we spoke briefly as the breathing required to talk generated pain in his stomach. Even though I understood the circumstances, I couldn't help but feel shut out. The urge to save and rescue had me battling myself. With Rich back in town and our summer of unwinding in full swing, I said nothing. It was stones and glass houses, pot meet kettle and all other hypocrisy adages.

It would be four months before I would see Scott again. By that time Rich had moved out. When Scott arrived, he looked exhausted from the hour drive to my place. He was also in a lot of pain. Each bump in the road jarred his recovering and still fragile insides. He was weaker than I expected and said it was because he couldn't eat very much while his stomach continued to heal and figured out how to work again. He had lost thirty-five pounds. My weight still down I felt like we were both laid bare, somehow more vulnerable and visible.

We sat quietly next to each other, holding hands. After a bit, he said, "I don't know what I'm in for other than a lot more recuperation. The docs say it will be a year before I am back to normal and I will have to sleep sitting up for the rest of my life. Part of the torn esophagus that was removed included that handy little valve that keeps your stomach contents in your stomach after you eat." He paused and looked around the room, as if looking to see if any evidence of Rich remained. It didn't. Then he said softly, his words a caress of permission, "If your heart needs to go somewhere else, I understand."

I pride myself on "being there"—as in I don't run when it gets hard. My friends and family can count on me when the chips are down. I wasn't about to bail because of a few challenges. The idea of finding a new love, one who wanted children, to start over with at this stage was also more than daunting. In that moment I doubled-down on our vision of that life we had both said we wanted.

"I don't want to go anywhere else, Scott. I *love* you. I want that life we talked about before your explosion. I *want* that life." Tears streamed down my face. And all the while, I couldn't shake a sense of guilt that my trips to Canada to see Rich had added to Scott's stress, pushing him over the edge.

Now, several years later, with some traction under our relationship, his return to work and some semblance of a new normal, I was the one dealing with doctors.

The elevator dinged. "I have to go. I'm supposed to be in the waiting room." My voice softened in response to his words, "I'd rather have you healthy and whole than no you and ten children."

I pressed "off" on my phone, looked at the open elevator door and then at my watch, and thought about leaving. Surely, I could miss this dermatology appointment. But Thursday mornings are usually filled with client calls, and it takes me a lot of organizing to schedule a day for doctor appointments. So I turned around and went back into the waiting room just as my name was called.

CHAPTER 6

Connecting the Dots

For the second time that day, my body was examined. Between measuring mole sizes and noting the changes in my chart, Dr. B asked me how I was. Standing, legs apart, my naked back to her, I blurted the morning's news about the growth on my ovary and the impending surgery. She stopped the exam and rolled her stool around to face me, motioning me to sit down on the table. As if trying to imprint onto my brain the importance of each word, she slowly said, "Do everything the doctor says to do. I didn't, and it was a mistake. I waited for a convenient time to have surgery and wound up with half my bladder, chemo, radiation and more than six months off work."

I nodded as she looked at me, her forehead furrowed with concern, though I kept thinking, "This isn't the same thing." But her wig scared me. She'd been wearing it for a year.

She rolled away, motioned me to stand up and went back to noting any changes in my moles from last year.

In a strange moment of connecting the dots I said, "Dr. B, I know both you and Dr. K from WRS (Women's Referral

Service)!" She smiled and nodded, asking me how Dr. K was doing. I ignored her question, continuing, "Nancy (WRS's founder) started the organization because she was frustrated at not being able to find a female doctor in the 1970's." I was certain there was some constellation of significance in meeting with both my doctors that day, both of whom I'd met through WRS, and in the order in which I had scheduled the appointments, but my brain felt too full to make sense of it.

I thanked Dr. B for sharing her story and assured her I was not going to mess around. "Good," she said, filling my bag with extra samples of moisturizers and sunscreens.

Next up: late breakfast with one of my dear goddess-sister-friends. I'd given her the news of the growth on my drive to the dermatologist, to warn her I might not be my usual, available, jovial self. I arrived in the parking lot a few minutes early and glanced in the rearview mirror to see how "the news" looked on my face. "Not good, but not too bad all things considered," I said aloud. In the mirror's reflection I saw a sign in the café window behind me that said "Wi-Fi Available!" I slapped on some lipstick, grabbed my laptop and purse and dashed in.

I asked for the corner spot: half booth and half table. I sat on the booth side, in the exact corner, able to see everything coming my way. I felt like an animal nesting, protecting. What exactly was I protecting myself from inside an L.A. breakfast café on Wilshire and Doheny? Screenwriters? Actors? Yes, a very scary lot, I thought.

I scanned my email inbox for new messages, hoping for the comfort of connection. Scott emailed that he was sending me the best possible vibes ever to exist in the world. I emailed back that I was indulging in the comfort of a warm lemon poppy seed muffin despite gluten and yeast intolerance. His instant reply: GOOD!

The café door opened with a whoosh and my friend strode in. She beamed her love at me and hugged me tight. I could see in her steady gaze and resolved jaw line that I would have all the support I might need, and she herself would see to it.

Flint and I talked about a friend she had supported through the indignities of chemo for ovarian cancer who is still here; in fact, who is thriving. I tried not to imagine myself bald as we talked about the ceremony our friend underwent to shave and henna tattoo her head. She wanted to be in charge of what happened to her hair before she lost it.

Maybe it was Flint's steadfastness, maybe it was my intuition, or something else altogether, but as we spoke of all the scenarios possible; I continued to have the sensation that I was not in a life-threatening situation. Nor did I care when people in the café stared in my direction when I began to cry as I told Flint that cancer was the least of my worries. I knew that my ovaries were almost out of gas and after each month's cycle, begged them to remain healthy and fertile.

"I know. I know, Kit-Cat. I know," she said softly as she reached across the table and held my hand. Some far away consciousness noticed I couldn't really *feel* her hand squeeze then, or her hug as we said goodbye in the parking lot after lunch.

I got in my car and sat for a moment. "Breathe, Cat. Breathe," I instructed myself. I began taking deep breaths. Someone behind me honked during the second breath, as if to say, "Lady, if you're leaving, leave already!" I motioned, *nicely*, that I wasn't leaving and continued to breathe deeply, wondering whether to go to my next appointment. I glanced at my watch, still feeling like I should be at home on a Thursday, working with clients. I retrieved my cell from the cavern of my purse and saw a few missed calls from my love.

"How are you doing?" he asked when I rang him back.

I didn't really know how I was doing so I said, "I am about to partake in one of your Christmas presents to me—the first facial in that series of three. When I booked it, I didn't know how much I'd need the pampering."

CHAPTER 7

Distraction

"Stay present, stay present, stay present, Cat," I silently intoned as the heavily accented Russian esthetician's quick yet gentle hands cleaned, exfoliated and super-moisturized my face and neck. In spite of my mantra, under the warm towels I drifted back to my ever-growing mental list of questions to ask the doctor. Shortening my mantra to, "Now . . . now . . . now . . ." I conjured up Eckhart Tolle's infectious laugh that I had listened to raptly on the audio version of *A New Earth*, along with his edict to be in the present moment.

Grateful for years of meditation and mindfulness workshops, I refocused on the quick-quick-slow-slow strokes of the esthetician's hands massaging my neck. I envisioned my muscles unwinding and tried to identify the sweet aromas drifting above my nose. When the invader questions tried to return, I refocused, again, this time on the cooling sensation of the thick, orange-scented cream she layered on my face. Letting the cream absorb, the esthetician rolled away from me on her stool, while the orange scent lulled me into peacefulness.

Though I didn't sleep, my brain stopped spinning and I entered the meditative zone I call drift.

Too soon I heard her stool wheels squeak back toward me. "OK, done," she said. She snatched the blanket from my finally relaxed body, and I slammed into reality. Without the blanket, I felt strangely naked, despite being swaddled in a strapless baby-pink terry-cloth wrap held firmly closed with three inches of Velcro.

She sat me up from my bliss and held a lighted hand mirror six inches from my nose to show me how youthful my face looked. I couldn't really see in the dim light but nodded in agreement. I started to stand, but she pushed me back down and arranged the hand mirror so I could continue to look. "The magic of this dewy, youthful look is the new anti-wrinkle serum, Instantly Ageless," she exclaimed.

She put down the mirror and held up the bottle of serum for me to admire, stroking it in the way *The Price is Right* gals do with everything from luggage to cars. Unlike the happy-go-lucky product models on game shows, my Russian esthetician had the intensity of a prison guard. Still feeling slightly exposed, I handed over my credit card to pay for the exorbitantly priced wonder serum, secretly hoping for a different kind of miracle.

I know I'm not the only woman whose default salve to emotional upheaval is spending money on things guaranteed to lift me up. Though the lift is temporary and does not answer my heart's cry of fear, vulnerability, or unmet desire, I keep doing it. My makeup drawers hold an array of expensive and pretty containers with bright shades of blush and eye shadow, all unused save for the one or two times I bravely tried to mix them with my customary neutral palette. Tags still on clothes that will never suit, hang in closets, mocking me ever so slightly when I look at them. It's as if the make-up and clothes are the answer to what I perceive is wrong . . . with relationships, with circumstances, with me.

I have this inner critic and survivor who can insist that I hide behind an array of masks to cover my feelings and over-come my fears. It's a bit like in the early days of theatre when performers wore masks to help convey the archetypal nature of their characters. I have discovered my own collection of masks and found they have been there since I was a little girl. Our psyches are smart, actually. When life gets scary, masks are born to keep us moving forward, as safely as possible.

My masks rise up when I feel the need to hide behind something because I feel too vulnerable. When I don't really feel like I know what I'm doing, or that other people don't know what they are doing, the Chief Operating Officer of Control mask rises. That mask hides my wide-eyed terror around feeling a lack of control and has me look like I am one calm, cool cucumber in charge, sometimes barking orders. When I don the Fairytale Fine mask, my natural optimism has spiraled into overdrive to overcome a sense of impending doom, so I can keep putting one foot in front of the other. And when I sense that if I help someone else get what he or she wants, they will give me what I want, the Suck It Up Buttercup mask rises up. When external circumstances or internal emotions feel out of control, up pops a mask.

My Chief Operating Officer of Control definitely rose up after Dr. K said: stages, baggie and rupture. The COOC commanded me to, "Buy the half an ounce, $200.00 anti-wrinkle miracle."

To this day, "Instantly Ageless" anti-wrinkle serum sits on the top shelf of my bathroom medicine cabinet, still in its shrink-wrap, next to the baby-pink, very potent, guaranteed to take off waterproof anything, eye-makeup remover.

I'm quite certain I wouldn't have sprung for the serum had I not been trying to erase fears of cancer. I'm quite certain if I *had* splurged on the serum just because, I would have at least tried the darn product since it wouldn't be attached to the news of the day.

My scheduled appointments completed, I sat in my car parked on California's quintessential palm-tree lined Beverly Drive, not sure what to do or which direction to turn. I pulled out my day planner. I wanted to capture the questions for my doctor that had been circling my brain all afternoon. Once my list was on paper, I called Dr. K's office but she was gone for the day. I felt an odd relief.

"Dr. K said something about getting a second opinion—would she refer me to anyone for that?" I asked the young woman who answered the phone. "I don't know, I'm only the accountant, in on Thursday afternoons. I'll leave her a message though." I hung up feeling ill. I didn't want a second opinion. That was my mother's question, not mine. I don't even want the damn opinion I already have I thought.

Still sitting in my car I called two more goddess-sister-friends with my news, each imploring me to stay in town with her rather than make the hour drive north to Ventura County. I thanked them and said, "No, I'm going home."

But I craved routine. So I called Veronica for the second time that day, and asked, "Daily Grill?" She said, "7:00."

Over our usual dinners—steak for her, salmon for me, she made the same offer.

"Honey, I think you should just stay with me. We can watch a movie." She has better electronic gear than most guys I know and always has several movies saved on her DVR and never minds re-watching one when I'm in town.

I love our "slumber party" nights of goofy rom-coms and action movies, talking into the wee hours. We always wind up laughing about how we lost our cool with someone, "sliding down the banister from spiritual orange-robed-monk-like awareness" and into the muck and mess of emotion-fueled life.

"Thank you honey, but all I want is to be home," I replied. Many times, I've found myself wishing I had moved back to the L.A. environ right after Rich and I broke up. But for years I'd longed to live at the beach and had finally found an affordable place to fulfill that longing. Besides, I wanted my next move to be into that house with Scott. Well, not the exact house he'd shown me prior, but still, a home together. It was definitely a trade-off—my cherished, affordable beach home in Ventura County an hour north of L.A. versus living closer to my circle of goddess-sister-friends and to Scott. I told Veronica I was imagining lounging on my high balcony chair, feet up on the rail, listening for messages in the waves. I told her that I longed to tap into the peacefulness that comes when I watch the stars move across the night sky over the Pacific. She nodded, understanding my nesting urge.

Most of all, I wanted to be nestled in my sweetie's arms. "Scott's coming up to be with me." She smiled. Sister-friends understand such things without feeling slighted or insulted.

Maybe because I'd made the drive so many times in the prior three and a half years, or maybe because I was distracted, or maybe because at nine o'clock at night there was no traffic to contend with, I remember nothing about driving home.

I felt glacially numb when I walked in the door, Scott arriving just minutes after me. We sat next to each other on my happy-looking yellow and gold striped down sofa, illuminated only by a small lamp with a low-wattage bulb. Scott's arm slid around my shoulders. I nestled into the space between his chest and shoulder; my clenched stomach feeling as if it had expelled a hard rock. The glacier inside me began to melt.

Scott's usually focused eyes were soft and hooded, his thick hair falling across a forehead tense with worry. I loved that his mouth refused to turn down, curling up ever so slightly in a show of optimism. I loved, too, that he let me weep in silence in his arms until I was moved to say something. He knew there were no words to solve the problem or fix me.

"I don't think I have cancer," I mumbled into his chest.

"That's good," he replied.

"I am scared about something happening during the proce-dure, like Dr. K winds up having to take my ovary." I moved my head, trying to find a dry place on his shirt to cry into.

"What if . . ." I stopped, not wanting to finish the sentence, afraid to speak my deepest fears about surgical complications, about actually having cancer, about chemo's side effects on fertility, about all the scenarios that had burned awful images in my mind since I heard the word surgery eleven hours before. I was afraid to speak any of these fears, or the bigger one that haunted me daily: Why did I wait? I was also afraid to speak because my twenty-plus-year spiritual journey and my seventeen years of being a coach had taught me that words are powerful. I didn't want to give my fears any more substance than they already had.

In response to all my unspoken what-ifs about complications, cancer and chemo, Scott tightened his arms around me, pulling me closer into him and said, "It won't." My body felt a relief-inspiring mix of his conviction, love and bravado in those two words and I relaxed into him even more deeply.

Usually, such short man-answers drive me mad. That night, I appreciated them. In fact, I think I loved him even more because he did not offer one stupid platitude while he held me and supplied a never-ending stream of Kleenex.

His hug and kiss before he left for work the next morning seemed, well, extra tender. "We'll get through this," he said, his voice at once melancholy and strong. He believed I was going to be fine, would remain fertile, that he'd continue his recovery, and we'd be OK. We both needed to believe that. We both needed to believe our vision of having a family was more than a fantasy. When friends (with and without kids) tried to talk to me about the improbabilities of this vision, given Scott's life-altering medical prognosis, or told me raising kids was for young people, I thanked them for their concern. Internally, I brushed off their words knowing I never did things according to "normal" or "the rules." I was in great physical shape and trusted that had to count for something. I also believed in intention, luck, and miracles. Not in a unicorn way, but in an experiential way. I had defied many an odd, including living through a terrible car accident with a train. So, I continued to believe that Scott and I would find our footing. I continued to believe what we set out to create would, indeed, become reality.

CHAPTER 8

Decisions

I longed to be able to pick up the phone and call my father. As Chief of Surgery in our Texas town of 68,000, I knew he would have offered up calm guidance with his authoritative yet kind tone. I grew up steeped in the miracles of Western medicine. My parents both avid readers and life-long learners, the family room coffee table featured the latest issue of *Annals of Surgery* mixed in with the most recent offering from the Book of the Month Club, as well as *Better Homes & Gardens, McCall's, Sports Illustrated, Saltwater Fisherman, National Geographic, LIFE,* and assorted gardening magazines.

Since I couldn't call Daddy, I sat on my high balcony chair overlooking the Pacific Ocean. Feet resting on the railing, I lounged back almost able to hear my father's soft whistling of made-up songs coming from the ether. I took a sip of coffee and focused my attention back to the waves rolling in just like they did every morning. The everyday ups and downs of mere mortals do not alter a wave's ceaseless journey of rising to meet the air and sun.

"What am I rising to meet? Who do I want to be through this?" I smiled, realizing I'd asked myself two very coach-style powerful questions: the type I'd ask a client facing a similar challenge.

A wave of tingly energy ran over my skin. JoyFullLight, one of my guides, my Future Self actually, dressed in her off-white diaphanous goddess dress, joined me on the balcony.

I first met JoyFullLight in 1996 during a guided visualization. The idea is there lives within each one of us a Future Self who knows the way forward when we feel lost in the here and now. A Future Self is a wiser, older, more seasoned version of us that offers guidance, self-assurance, and comfort. I have friends and clients who have changed their names, spouses, careers, and lives shortly after I guided them to meet their Future Self. My relationship with JoyFullLight has helped me to cut ties with toxic situations and people, to honor the core of who I am, and to believe in myself when the evidence led elsewhere. I spoke with her daily as Rich and I navigated our painful parting. Yes, I have developed an outrageously deep relationship with the energy that is JoyFullLight. She looks like me about twenty years down the road and exhibits a constant serenity to which I aspire.

When I met JoyFullLight during that initial guided visualization, I saw her living in a beach home with a stunning view of the Pacific Ocean. The first day I walked through the door of my current home, with Rich and the real estate agent, I gasped with the delight of a child. In that moment, I knew JoyFullLight had led me to find this idyllic, and perfectly affordable beach home. It was sad and telling that Rich left so soon after we got there. He loved mountains and lakes. I loved the beach. I believed JoyFullLight wanted to make sure I would have access to the solace and comfort the beach brings me as I grappled with my broken heartedness.

Only JoyFullLight could have arranged the sequence of outwardly coincidental events that led me to a small seaside town I had never heard of, just an hour away from where Rich and I had lived for twelve of our seventeen years, and have me moved in within three weeks. It began during the previous full moon gathering with my goddess friends, when I declared, "Rich and I are looking for a new place and I have laid down the law—it is time for me to be at the beach. Please hold that intention with me." One of the goddesses replied, "I have a friend leasing a condo on the beach in Ventura! I'll give you her number." I called the leasing agent and got the address. On the appointed day we drove up to Ventura and sat and waited at the gate to the complex. We were entranced by the beautiful landscaping, the hundred-yard proximity to the pier and beach, and all just an hour's drive from L.A.'s San Fernando Valley. After waiting ten minutes, I phoned the agent and when I asked if she was running late, she told me we were at the wrong complex. We followed her directions and drove to a complex a block away. My heart fell: no lush landscaping, an unattractive exterior and the unit itself a no-go. I began to cry and Rich said, "Let's go back to the other place." He had noticed the large encased bulletin board with flyers announcing available units. We called the number of the leasing agent, never thinking in a million years he'd answer on a Sunday morning. Within an hour, we had negotiated the deal.

Leaning back in my balcony chair, I said, "Hello, JoyFullLight," and closed my eyes. Though she is not a physical body, my deep relationship with her has me experience her as an embodied energy. So it was not unusual to "feel" her standing beside me and experience an imaginary sense of her stroking my hair comfortingly. A bit of her serenity awakened in me. I then imagined her relaxing into the other tall balcony chair and gazing at me with such love and gentleness that a sense of peace swept through me. In that moment I realized how far away I'd gotten from her energy lately. Her un-beckoned appearance reminded me to consider all parts of me. "Yes, I want to be you through this experience," I said out loud.

"You are the daughter of a surgeon," she whispered inside my head, smiling at me from across the table.

"Yes, I am the daughter of a surgeon," I replied inside myself, longing again to call my daddy.

She continued, "You are a believer in Western medicine's ability to save lives during emergencies."

"Yes, I am a believer in Western medicine's ability to save lives." I snorted and said, "I am also the *recipient* of Western medicine's brilliance at fixing broken bones," running my fingertips the length of my right thigh, as if tracing the pin inside my femur, one of the surgical results from the car-train wreck.

"You are a priestess," she wrote very slowly on the screen of my mind. Then she invited, "Tell me everything you are."

Eyes still closed I removed my feet from the balcony rail and sat up. I thought about all the full moon ceremonies I had facilitated. "I am a priestess," I said out loud. I thought about the three levels of Reiki training and initiations and said, "I am a healer." I thought about becoming a certified coach, and all the courses I'd led and taken in that field since and said, "I am a coach." I thought of all the workshops, keynotes, and retreats I'd led and said, "I am a teacher."

JoyFulllLight looked at me and smiled, prompting me to continue with a nod. "I am a believer in alternative medicine's ability to heal lives. I am the recipient of alternative medicine's brilliance in naturally balancing the body." She used the worldwide gesture to continue, rolling her right hand in forward motion circles. I continued more quickly and playfully, "I am a believer in 'laying on of hands' healing, prayer, meditation, love, optimism, saying yes often, taking risks, astrology, numerology, nutrition and visualization. I am a believer in combining the best of Western, Eastern and alternative medicines!"

The message received, the messenger slipped off to the future. JoyFulllLight doesn't hang around all day, and I make up that she must be very busy in the future, no doubt arranging for my next home with a stunning view to appear.

I felt a little torn by what I had given voice to with JoyFulllLight's prompting, and I ached inside to speak to my father. What advice would he offer me? Would he tell me to trust the voice within?

Coffee cup empty, I went inside to replenish it and decided instead to unpack the tote bags I dropped as soon as I'd walked in the door the night before. Empty water bottles into the recycle bin, laptop unpacked and turned on, I hung up my sweater and pulled the vial of Instantly Ageless serum from its lunch-bag size white sack. I walked into my bathroom and put the bottle on the top shelf, next to the no-fooling-around eye-makeup remover. I looked in the mirror. I didn't look any different than I had the morning before, except for the red, swollen, I'm-too-old-to-cry-that-hard eyes.

I leaned into the tub and turned on the water. I decided to feel no guilt for the very long, very hot shower I was about to take, despite California's perennial water shortage. Evoking the priestess in me, the one who believes that all of earth's elements offer magic and power, I stood under the steaming stream, asking it to wash away my fear. I envisioned it swirling down the drain as I rinsed shampoo and conditioner from my hair. I envisioned the organic lavender body wash removing fear from my skin, so that it flowed as bubbles down the drain.

Cleansed, I placed my palms on my heart chakra, between my breasts, water streaming over my body, "Kuan Yin, goddess of women's self-love and self-healing, please come to me now and rinse me with your love, your grace, your healing waters."

I felt her gentle presence surround me. She was in the drops of water cascading over my skin. She was in the mist rising up from the heat, penetrating my lungs.

Remembering the power of the waterfall at the Iao Needle state park on Maui, I imagined standing under it now. "Kuan Yin, please purify and cleanse away the underlying cause of the physical manifestation of the growth on my right ovary. Please surround my heart and ovary with your teachings of self-love and self-healing. I am willing to grow and learn. I am willing to . . . huh?" My trance-like prayer was broken by my linear mind, and I stood there dumbstruck, asking myself the question, "What am I willing to do for my health?"

"Fight for it" didn't feel easy or fun. "Do nothing," wasn't an option. "Ask for help," felt good, though stunningly unfamiliar.

I closed my eyes again, my hand still on my heart chakra. "Ask for help. Yes, I'm willing to ask for help from my goddess sisters. Yes, I am willing to ask for help and I am willing to heal myself to wholeness."

DECISIONS

I began composing the email in my head to my goddess sisters as I towel dried my hair.

Kuan Yin smiled and nodded her approval.

CHAPTER 9

The Healing Chamber
- Calling the Circle

Email, Friday, March 4

Dear Ones,

I am calling a healing circle for myself . . . which feels more than odd. And, I'm doing it anyway. Gather at Veronica's on Sunday, March 6, at 1:30.

In January, my doc discovered an ovarian cyst (not unheard of for me) and the follow-up yesterday revealed it is still there, and not looking like a typical fluid-filled cyst. The ultrasound makes it look like the growth is tissue filled. (From the look on my doc's face, I knew that wasn't good.)

I'm looking at probable surgery as soon as possible. She might have to take the ovary as well. I'm sure you all know where that has me spinning. The good news in all of this is if it is something to be concerned about, we are catching it v-e-r-y early.

I'm gathering the circle for two reasons.

1. A Miracle! I'm asking you to be my healing surgeons and blast the thing with healing energy to remove the growth or whatever it is, non-surgically! I totally believe it can be done and ask for your help.

2. Healing! I am ready, willing, and wanting to heal!

Please let me know if you can be there. Oh, bring a nosh so we can ground with food after we perform the cyst exorcism!

Love and hugs,

Cat

I call it "Circle Up" when "the goddesses" come together as a group to tend to a sister. Our spouses, lovers and other groups of friends know whom "the goddesses" are when referred to as "the goddesses." This group of twelve sister-friends formed as the result of the first Modern Goddess workshop I created, which culminated in a full moon ceremony. I'd never led one before, but was assured by the wise voice within me, JoyFullLight, that I absolutely knew how. She was right. When the first full moon ceremony came to an end, someone said, "Can we do this again next month?" I said, "Sure!" Hundreds of women have been invited to sit in those full moon circles with us through the years, and twelve of us have maintained the kind of deep friendship that doesn't need questioning, despite our widely varied personalities, opinions and styles. When one of us puts out the call to support her latest endeavor, be it a fundraiser, performance of some sort, or a workshop, we show up. We've gathered in healing circles to comfort a sister going through breast cancer; we've gathered to help sisters grieve the loss of a parent and a beloved four-legged friend; we've gathered for milestone birthdays and over cocktails to help mend a broken heart or navigate a work crisis.

This was the first time I had sent an email requesting a Circle Up for myself.

Each one of my goddess-sisters is scrappy, smart and unafraid of working her butt off to achieve her dreams. We are from all over —the Midwest, the Southwest, the Pacific Northwest, and yes, some are L.A. natives. Many make their living in the arts—theatre, film, TV. Some are entrepreneurial like me, and others work in a more traditional work environment. Veronica combines being a savvy businesswoman in the medical field along with her many creative passions. From modest beginnings, Veronica worked her way up and decided to buy a place after the earthquake in Northridge, CA, when real estate prices took a nosedive. I was with her the day she discovered what is now her beautiful, goddess townhome. I couldn't see its potential under the awful wallpaper, carpet and paint colors, but she did. And since 2002, when I moved with Rich from L.A. proper to Lake Elsinore, her Studio City townhouse became our de-facto gathering spot.

Veronica's home is infused with all manner of Spirit and goddess energy from the dozens of full moon ceremonies performed in front of the living room fireplace. Artemis, Aphrodite and The Three Graces statues cast in plaster and stone stand as sentinels for our ceremonies. Lovers in an angled embraced and cast of copper remind us of passion's power. A 3-D mermaid head with a Mona Lisa-like smile and wild sculpted hair greets anyone going up or down the staircase. A well-stocked, marble-top cabinet bar separates the dining and living rooms. Traditional crystal, silver and china pieces are displayed in the top part of the black lacquer china hutch. I love that I know one of the cabinets below holds phone books and large three-ring binders. I also know one of the three silverware-drawers holds hammers, screwdrivers and other hardware supplies like batteries and light bulbs.

Eight of my goddess sisters were in town and available the day of my healing circle. The dining room table filled with a potluck feast: salads of different kinds, a casserole of homegrown squash, zucchini, onions and peppers, and of course, no goddess potluck is complete without at least two or three varieties of dessert—homemade gluten-free apple cobbler, brownies and cut up melon. The food and space were abundant and eclectic, and so were we as we gathered in sacred circle.

In her managerial "let's get going" mode, Veronica called for a sushi delivery and then double folded a king size bedspread and laid it on the floor, signaling the start. Another sister took my hand and walked me toward the pallet, and I lay down.

"Do you want one or two pillows under your head?" asked one sister.

"Just one, thank you," I replied. I was nervous and certain at the same time—nervous because I'd never called a Circle Up for myself and certain that the love of these women was exactly what I needed to free up . . . something . . . even though I wasn't exactly sure what yet.

Another sister healer placed two pillows under my knees for maximum support and comfort as the rest gathered around me. A red fleece throw was draped gently over my legs and feet. An oblong circle formed around me as each sister sat cross-legged on the floor—one at my head, one at my feet and three on either side of me. We began to breathe slowly in unison and in just a few moments, the peace of ceremony enveloped us.

My sisters' bodies become sacred healing chamber walls, erected around me, at once protective and holy. I instructed my Chief Operating Officer of Control take-charge brain to be quiet, desperately looking for the off switch. "Ask me nicely!" said the saucy voice in my brain. I obliged: "Please relax so we can concentrate on being cocooned in this healing chamber." My brain voice smiled and exhaled. It likes to concentrate.

Good grief, I am so much more comfortable sitting cross-legged on the floor as part of a healing vessel for someone else. I felt out-of-body as I lay there, nervously anticipating the gift I had asked for and was about to receive. Tamara, a minister's daughter, asked if I wanted to lead or if I wanted someone else to take on that role. "Someone else, please." She smiled and nodded.

I closed my eyes, relinquishing the priestess roll as Tamara focused our attention by instructing, " . . . take a deep breath, slowly inhale. Now exhale any tension."

I imagined myself as rose buds in a continual state of opening. The first bud opened in the middle of my forehead, (my third eye, or mind's eye). Next, a bud opened in my heart, then one in my womb, and with each inhale I imagined this opening energy infusing all of my body's cells.

Tamara, the priestess for this healing chamber, continued the benediction, "We gather around Cat as her healers, her friends, her sisters, and we do so with the intention of full, complete healing. We ask that our hands and energy be guided for Cat's highest good."

As her words focused my healers, I too focused my thoughts and feelings. I chimed in sharing that I thought there was some anger to vanquish and some remnant squishy grief to release as well.

"Okay, goddesses, do what you do best," I said.

I heard several rubbing their hands together to get the energy flowing and after another few deep breaths, in unison, eight pairs of loving hands approached my body. I felt the heat of healing energy stream from my healers' hands into my body. Some laid their hands directly on my body while other hands hovered as much as a foot above it. All my goddess sisters became physical conduits for energy to pour from some ethereal source through them and into me. One hand placed on my heart-center felt comfortingly warm, and another hand on my neck felt like bubbles tickling my throat. Then a pair of hands pulled energy from my heart as if picking lint from my shirt with a series of rapid little pinches and pulls. My chest rippled with a wave of release of what felt like a burst of volatile, white-hot rage. Mentally, I chanted a prayer to turn on my own flow of Reiki energy so I could participate in my healing.

Even though my eyes were closed, I could feel my healers' intuitive coordination. The healer at my head pulsed her hands rhythmically on the tops of my shoulders, alternating sending energy from my right shoulder down my body and then from my left shoulder. Simultaneously, the healer at my feet released the energy pulse by "sweeping" the bottom of my foot and plucking the energy out as if playing a harp string. A space in-between the shoulder pulse allowed for the energy to travel down me before it was plucked from my foot. I smiled and enjoyed the partnership of my healers. At one point I could only feel six sets of hands on me and knew two of my healers were sitting back in a meditative state visualizing my healed body, probably with arms open and lifted, as if about to embrace a loved one.

My wet, salty release of grief began as six hands were gently stacked—three on my heart and three on my throat. When placed on my ovaries and womb, their hands unleashed fear and panic. I longed to curl into a fetal position or kick and scream. Instead, I mentally repeated the mantra, "Stay. Stay. Stay." I remained on my back, experiencing all of it. On the screen of my inner eye, the regret-inducing circumstances with Daddy, Rich and Scott raced by. I did not allow myself to press the pause button. I'd been pressing that damn pause button too often and was living the imbalance of too much self-recrimination. It felt timely to face my regrets and let them go.

I ping-ponged between experiencing myself as a block of ice as I released my panic and fear and experiencing myself as fire when rage and grief coursed through me. I didn't kick off the red fleece throw, choosing to sweat out the heat of the fiery emotions. A sister placed one of her most sacred objects in my right sweaty palm and curled my fingers around it. I smiled in recognition of the gift of the cool brass horse figurine.

Next a pair of gentle yet firm hands pressed on my right ovary and heart simultaneously. "Breathe Cat, just keep breathing," I said silently when the pressure on my ovary created another panicky, claustrophobic sensation. I wanted to scream, "Don't put pressure there," remembering what my doctor had said, "First we'll baggie the ovary and growth to keep any rupture contained," but I chose trust.

When those pressing hands lifted, the lint picker plucked more emotions from my heart. It felt like silly string sprayed out of my heart with each pinch and pluck, releasing more of my un-silly anger. I exhaled loudly. We began to inhale and exhale together, loudly and rhythmically, my healers' breaths becoming additional conduits to help me release my anger, no doubt releasing some of theirs, too.

Floating in my drifty, slightly light-headed altered deep-breathing state I heard the phrase, "All Love, All The Time," as if spoken by a Spirit DJ for KLUV FM. I heard my laugh and even with my eyes still closed I could sense my healers looking at me. I repeated the phrase I'd just heard in my best late-night DJ voice, and we all riffed on the idea as a new bumper sticker slogan. I felt the heat in their hands increase. "What a great internet radio station!" someone said. "This is KLUV, All Love, All the Time, our lines are open for your requests," I offered. More laughter. More love. More release. More healing.

Amidst all the laughter, the doorbell rang. The delivery guy bearing sushi arrived early or late or maybe at the perfect time, who knows? I do know he got an eyeful when Veronica opened the door because our healing chamber was camped in full view of the entry. The healing continued as the delivery guy ran the credit card. I sensed two healers rise from sitting to kneeling to work with the energy above my physical body. Others were still touching my heart-center, right ovary, forehead and throat. And we were still laughing from "All Love, All the Time"; it was like we had the church giggles and couldn't stop if we tried. One of my healing chamber walls playfully invited the delivery guy to join us! I'm not sure what we'd have done if he'd said "yes!"

When Veronica returned to the healing circle, it was as if my healers made a decision: rather than let the sushi delivery halt or disrupt the healing, they amped it up. I experienced a crescendo that caused my body to shudder as all the energy in and around me came together. Shaking, I took a slow, deep breath and felt more open space inside me than I'd felt in a long time. I began to experience my healers' love inside the open spaces. I knew I was physically experiencing their love because enough of the other stuff that was not love was gone. In a seamless shift, my healing ceremony came to a close organically as each healer in her own time removed her hands from my body and sat back in meditative contemplation or prayer.

Gratitude began to stream from my eyes and roll into my ears. I remained on my back, eyes closed, while each of my healers shared what she saw or felt during the ceremony.

"Oh, Catamaran, I saw you holding a gorgeous toddler, with curly blonde hair and your sweet smile," said one of the goddesses named Connie. (There are two in our circle of friends named Connie!)

"I saw your ovary as perfect and whole and alone, as in growth-free," said another.

Two named other loved ones for us to send healing energy to, and so we did, expanding the healing chamber. That's the thing about healing energy, it wants to spread and go viral.

I sat up and looked at each one of my goddess-sister-healers in turn, hoping my eyes conveyed my overwhelming and heartfelt gratitude. "Thank you," I whispered.

Veronica said, "Thank *you*, honey," and squeezed my hand tight. Then she stood up and said, "Let's eat! I'm starving!"

We were all a little misty eyed with gratitude and the abundance of love as we feasted. Balancing my plate of sushi, salad and veggie casserole on my lap, I said, "To have y'all in my life reminds me that my mom might just be right—I do indeed travel on a lucky star."

"Blessed be!" said Darlene.

CHAPTER 10

Widening the Net

I woke the morning after the Healing Circle to the aroma of the coffee Veronica made for me before she left for work. I smiled, and my first conscious thought felt like a Divine directive, "Widen your healing circle. Include CTI." (CTI is the acronym for The Coaches Training Institute*—one of the first coach training organizations, where I am a senior faculty member.) It is fair to say that meeting the founders of CTI before CTI was established was one of the biggest gifts of my life.

Henry Kimsey-House appeared in my life in 1992 when he led a workshop for the L.A. organization Women In Theatre. I attended the workshop because I was on the board of directors and I was fascinated by the topic: "Maintaining Your Dignity and Power During the Audition Process." I was just beginning to feel stronger in my Candida recovery and in my ability to hold my head above the waters of grief and deep failure from losing my father. During that workshop, Henry led a two-minute, life purpose visualization that changed the course of my life. I blurted my answer to his final question about what message you are on earth to share: "Know the light of love is inside. Share it!" It was as if all of me had been waiting for those words to tumble out of my mouth. As I spoke them, I experienced my inherent optimism, enthusiasm and passion. The exercise was designed to show actors that we were up to something bigger than an individual role in one film, TV show or play. The impact on me was even greater. It revealed the deepest truth of my being. I could stop looking to the outside world to comfort me, make me okay, forgive me, or anything else. I knew the more I focused on the love light inside me, the more I'd experience self-forgiveness, self-love and the love around me. It felt like I finally understood the message of every wisdom text, personal growth and psychological book I'd ever read, especially *A Return to Love* by Marianne Williamson, (which she based on the teachings of *A Course in Miracles*).

I jumped at the chance to do another, in depth two-day workshop with Henry when he came back to town. At the end of the workshop, I knew he had what I wanted. I don't mean him personally, but I wanted what he embodied, even if I couldn't have explained it back then. I hired Henry as my coach, not even knowing what that really meant. After two months of being coached, I said, "Henry, I do for almost everyone in my life what you are doing with me. I do it backstage, with friends on the phone, heck, even in bars over drinks! When they ask me what I think, I ask them what *they* already know!" He then issued a life-changing invitation: "My business partner Laura and I are going to teach a workshop on coaching skills next month—would you like to come to San Francisco for it?"

I went to that workshop, and then I went to every new course they offered. At the completion of the four courses, a group of us said, "We want more!" Heeding our desires, Henry, Laura Whitworth and Karen Kimsey (who would become Karen Kimsey-House) created a Coach Certification program. Honoring my background in theatre and improvisation training to say, "yes, and" to what is offered, I said a hardy yes to enrolling in the course, another hardy yes to becoming one of the first certified coaches, then a hell yes to becoming one of CTI's first faculty members for their Certification Program. Now, CTI offers courses in 16 countries, 13 languages and has trained more than 65,000 coaches.

I think of CTI as more than an organization for whom I do some training work. CTI is part home and family, part kick-in-the-ass-to-always-keep-evolving and part of my turn-around story.

At Veronica's I did a good job of ignoring my awakening directive for a few hours by meditating, journaling, sipping coffee and participating in my weekly writing group call. When I ran out of good-for-me things to do, I flipped my laptop open, clicked the "New Message," icon and became mesmerized by the blinking cursor in the empty email field. I wondered what the heck I could, or should, ask of my CTI family. It felt *almost* easy or at least natural to lean into my small circle of goddess-sister-friends, but to ask for help of so many! "Breathe, Cat. Feel your body," I told myself. Still experiencing surges of warmth and tingles in my womb space from the healing circle, I asked the tingles what words to speak.

The tingles had nothing to say. Disappointed, I started thinking about my cadre of powerful, intentional and miracle-producing coach trainer colleagues. And then it hit me: I was feeling awkward. I laughed out loud, sharing my mirth with

Veronica's statues and crystals. "I've never lost anyone to awkwardness yet," comes out of my mouth at least once a week in response to clients and coaches in training who feel uncomfortable trying something new.

So that is where I began—by owning up to how awkward it felt to ask them for help. I shared what was going on in my body and asked for prayers and healing energy focused on my ovary. I asked them to surround me in their love. After I clicked the send icon, I realized what I'd actually done. I'd given a modern-day update to the weekly snail-mailed church prayer list bulletin I had grown up with and morphed it into a group email plea for support. I rummaged in Veronica's kitchen for something to eat or drink, even though I wasn't hungry or thirsty. I wanted to distract myself. In a church bulletin, the recipient isn't asking for prayers directly. But I was. Even more uncomfortable was the thought that I had never met in person many of the people I was asking for help, love and healing energy.

There is a distinct paradox to being a professional coach. The work is solitary and loneliness can creep in from only talking on the phone, or even, as has become the case, via video. The flipside is having a large community of virtual colleagues. As I thought about my life that morning, I was humbled by how many circles of friends I had to lean into, both in-person and online. I also reflected on how hard I had worked to navigate and keep these relationships. A few years prior a big blow-up occurred inside my goddess-sister circle when some of us tried to start a business together. It took a year or so for the friction to cool off. I like to believe the warmth of our love allowed us to gradually put aside our individual hurts and focus on our collective goodness. My

CTI colleagues also fight on occasion. We are passionate about our work as coaches and trainers and there is just no way to agree all the time. I suppose the saving grace is that our potentially divisive opinions and needs rarely become more important than the whole. I needed the whole just then.

There is nothing to distract the mind like fresh ground almond butter eaten off a spoon, chased down by reheated coffee. I was so busy sucking the gooey goodness from my teeth and gums that by the time I returned to my computer I had almost forgotten what had driven me to the almond butter. I was surprised to find a dozen email messages from my colleagues. As I began to read them, another dozen popped into my inbox with that little "tink" announcement tone. Tink, tink, tink! I found myself scanning the emails, not taking in the magic; just going from one tink to the next.

"S-l-o-w-d-o-w-n, Cat." I obeyed my inner counsel, taking a deep breath and turning down the volume on my computer. Another deep breath and I began to read the emails with my full attention, hearing the sender's voice speak their words of love and inspiration to me. I read as slowly as I could, letting each image of love and healing melt into me as if savoring the finest chocolate. I experienced the light and love in their words like a protective cloak, wrapping me in radiant warmth. My mind became a movie screen for their descriptive pictures of my healed ovary loaded with eggs. Several missives made me laugh out loud with their wildly irreverent visuals—like the one from Henry of a giant Universal Hoover vacuum sucking the growth right off my ovary! I didn't realize I was crying until I tasted tears sliding into my laughing mouth.

One colleague's email made me sit up straight. All Grace did was share the name of a naturopathic doctor trained as a relationship coach, but the moment I read her words the proverbial hair on the back of my neck rose up. Out of the dozens of referrals and suggestions I received, this one lodged in my solar plexus, my gut instinct region, as the one to follow.

In that moment, I realized what was in front of me wasn't just about healing my ovary or even my fertility issue; it was the work I do every day with my women clients. It was tending to the relationship with my body by way of my Spirit, emotions and mind. It was about a radical change in how I'd been approaching my dreams, vision, and desires. What was in front of me was, above all, transforming the old to make way for the new. For the second time that day, it felt like I experienced a Divine directive. I *sensed* this naturopathic doctor would offer the non-invasive healing option I needed to explore next.

If I'd stopped to really think about it, my brain, indoctrinated by Western medicine, might have quarreled with my inner knowing and body wisdom. Healing from the Candida invasion and working seventeen years as a professional coach, however, had taught me to listen to my body. I knew deep in my being a naturopathic doctor relationship coach who lived 2800 miles away in Toronto, Canada, *could* hold the key to my healing. I emailed Dr. S right away.

Saturated with gratitude, I closed my laptop and got on with the rest of my day.

CTI rebranded in 2019 from Coaches Training Institute to the Co-Active Training Institute.

CHAPTER 11

Shifting Gears

First up when leaving Veronica's was errand running before heading south to Anaheim to join my future sister-in-law and her maid of honor. Months before, we'd planned a Disneyland bachelorette party . . . yes, a bachelorette party for a forty-something bride at Disneyland! We had laughed uproariously at the notion, "What happens in Disneyland, stays in Disneyland!"

While driving east on Riverside Drive in Toluca Lake (which is really just a fancy neighborhood name in Burbank) on my way to the bank, I was struck by the irony of going to kid central at this particular time "Well, Cat," my inner coach responded, "you can be annoyed, upset, disengaged and have a miserable time, or choose a different perspective."

Helping clients shift perspectives is one of my favorite things to do as a coach. The idea is to open up new ways of seeing a current situation when you are stuck in a rut of thinking and feeling. By acknowledging other ways to view a situation, energy gets freed up and new choices can be made. The result? From new thinking, new or different actions can be taken, which offer the opportunity for different internal experiences and external results. I ran through an assortment of other possible perspectives: Pissy—nope. Sad—nope. Scared—nope. Loving—mmm. Fun—mmm! Enjoyment. Big mmm-hmm! I decided the perspective of Enjoyment would allow me to look for opportunities to take pleasure in the whole experience, including being surrounded by children of all ages. That felt much better than grumpy. "Dang, this perspective-shifting-opening-up-new-possibilities thing really works," I joked out loud to myself.

My mobile phone rang as I pulled into the bank parking lot. Caller I.D. revealed my doctor's name, so I answered. I heard Joan, the surgical coordinator's usually kind voice say a brief, "Hi, Cat" before she quickly rattled off the date she'd set up for the surgery, when I had to do pre-op lab work, and something else I didn't hear because my chest tightened and a furious irritation rose up in me. It was clear she had picked the date convenient and available for the doctor and the hospital without consulting me about my schedule and convenience. While I knew it wasn't a personal slight, I rebelled. With a calm I didn't feel, I simply said, "No, not next week." There was a huge pause, the kind that makes you wonder if the cell gods frowned and you lost digital connection.

I told her the date that I was okay with which generated another huge pause. We went back and forth. The date I wanted to schedule was not available at the hospital of first choice. I didn't care and wondered how she knew that date was unavailable.

What I didn't tell her was I could still feel the effects of the healing circle at work in my body, that I was seeking the counsel of a naturopathic doctor and wanted to give these approaches time to work. We settled on March 25, the week of my birthday, the date I offered. I hung up the phone (hmm, do we really "hang up" a cell phone?) and wrote the date in my calendar and sang a sarcastic "Well, Happy Birthday to me."

I walked into the bank and smiled at the greeter, who wished me a good day. I then made a deposit and withdrew cash as if I hadn't just scheduled a surgical procedure and wasn't feeling threats to my fertility; it was as if I was certain I was perfectly healthy and normal. I got back in the car and headed south to Anaheim and thought how crazy I might seem to outside eyes. I had scheduled time off from clients and training gigs to go Disneyland in the middle of the week for a bachelorette gathering. I had just challenged the god-like stature of Western medicine's machine, and I planned to work with a naturopathic doctor by phone.

I called my mom on the drive south to give her the latest update. Though at this point in our adult relationship, she is one of my best friends, and we talk almost daily about any and everything; she sighed the Mom sigh.

"What?" I asked trying to sound casual.

"Cat, why are you delaying this? In some cases, weeks make a difference." I felt my customary rebellious irritation kick in, even as I realized she was expressing the depth of her concern about a delay in surgery. A friend of hers had recently gone through ovarian cancer and had been extremely frustrated that doctors had not figured out her six months of symptoms before the cancer had progressed. If my mom still smoked, I'm certain I would have heard the lighter click and a deep first drag on the cigarette.

"It's not like I'm waiting months. I only delayed it by eight days."

I could sense her wrestling her worry to the ground, knowing I wouldn't budge.

"Do you want me to come out there?"

My mom does hospital be-with better than anyone I know. She and I have both had to do it too many times. Keeping it light, I said, "Oh, Mom, thank you, but no. This is an in and out deal and Connie and Veronica and all the goddesses have offered to help with whatever needs handling." Plus, I didn't want to have to worry about my mom navigating airports alone or driving in L.A., both far from her comfort zone.

"Are you sure? I can be *your* very patient nurse for a change!" We laughed about how a pain or drug induced delirium caused her to be bossy, and I'd ignore or make fun of her "princess and the pea" requests to smooth out sheets and make sure hospital gown ties were not under her shoulders. It had begun with her sudden surgery for a ruptured disk that left her right leg numb, and the joke continued through her two knee replacements. Everyone in the family feels deep gratitude that she came through all those surgeries with few complications and many positive outcomes.

Our laughter eased the conversation into other topics like Disneyland and her search for a mother-of-the-groom dress suitable for a wedding on a New Orleans streetcar.

My next phone call was to Scott. In an overly soft tone, he indirectly questioned the wisdom of delaying the surgery, even though he was relieved that I wasn't having the surgery at the doctor's preferred hospital, as he knew someone who'd had a bad experience there. I repeated what I'd told my mom: delaying eight days is not a big deal, and he agreed.

"No more phone calls," I said out loud to myself. I wanted to spend some time in silence, knowing as soon as I arrived in Anaheim I'd be talking or listening non-stop. My mind drifted to what the next batch of emails from colleagues might say. I could feel the energy of their missives flying through the great World-Wide-Web toward me. I laughed at myself because in the span of several hours I'd gone from hesitant to email them at all, to looking forward to reading their replies. I was hoping for more notes that made me laugh, like the Universal Hoover image.

Reminding myself of my chosen perspective—Enjoyment—I took "The Happiest Place on Earth" exit off the I-5 freeway in Anaheim. I was making this up as I went, doing the next thing from a place of instinct. Right then, I decided to not apologize one more time for arriving in Anaheim a day later than planned. The lyrics to Frank Sinatra's "I Did It My Way" took on new meaning each time I followed my instincts.

CHAPTER 12

The Happiest Place on Earth

Imagine three women—a brunette (maid-of-honor), redhead (sister-in-law-to-be) and blonde (me)—walking astride. Lifting her hands to the breeze, the brunette says, "The air is so crisp, like fall!" The blonde points her nose skyward like a dog, "I love the way the air smells after it rains!" The redhead takes off her windbreaker and ties it around her waist, "The sun feels warm but not icky New Orleans humid hot!" We weren't in a Disneyland or Anaheim Chamber of Commerce commercial but agreed this might be the most perfect Southern California weather ever!

The brisk walk from our hotel to the park was good exercise. With approximately the same length legs, we set a rhythmic pace and agreed no gym would be required after a day of walking around "The Happiest Place on Earth." (As if we would actually hit the hotel's gym rather than happy hour.)

I hadn't been to Disneyland since visiting with my brother and his first wife nineteen years prior. The image of his first wife and me, both in our twenties and wearing mouse ears, popped into my mind, followed quickly by the thought that vendors should probably not sell mouse ears to adults with no kids in tow. After my Sunday evening healing circle, "All Love, All The Time," was my new mantra. Even so, approaching the park, I noticed I was unsettled by the talk I had with my mother the day before.

Walking in the bright sunshine, a deep sadness threatened to dislodge me from the peaceful zone gifted me by the healing circle and all the loving emails. I *intentionally* took a deep breath and rolled the mantra, "All Love, All the Time," and my chosen perspective, Enjoyment through my gray matter. I had done the same when I spoke with Joan, the surgical coordinator the day before; when a wedding drama was shared over dinner; when eating breakfast in the Anaheim hotel while the crap news network blared the depressing body count of soldiers killed in Afghanistan the day before.

"OK y'all were here yesterday, and I haven't been here in like a hundred years, so which rides might jostle me too much?" I wanted to protect my right ovary from excessive bumps or compression. Lisa and Carmen talked through the jerkiness of a few rides and told me the one roller coaster I should avoid (The Matterhorn) wasn't even open that week. "And if I were you, I'd forgo the elevator-like drop ride," said Lisa. That one, I assured them, wasn't even on my list.

Due to several cups of coffee with breakfast, the first stop in the park was the Ladies' room. The sparkly clean stall I entered had a stylish pair of sunglasses sitting on top of the toilet paper dispenser. We took them to Lost and Found and for our trouble we each were rewarded with, "Honorary Citizen" of Disneyland buttons! When the Disney-friendly gal behind the desk asked if we were celebrating anything special Lisa shared this outing was her bachelorette bash. Carmen and I chimed in with our joke, "What happens in Disneyland, stays in Disneyland!" Carmen had also gotten engaged recently, so Lisa and Carmen both received "Getting Married" and "Engaged" buttons to wear along with their "Honorary Citizen" button. Ms. Disney Friendly flashed her own engagement rock and giggled.

I had nothing to say. Listening to their proposal stories, wedding dates and dress dramas, I found myself shifting my weight from one foot to the other, subtly moving toward the door yet unable to find an escape from the taunting thoughts in my head. I usually feel like I belong in groups of women, but with no ring, I didn't belong in this circle.

My Enjoyment perspective began to wane under a litany of self-doubt: What the hell? I'm a good person. I'm told I'm attractive, smart, funny, sweet, caring. From both Rich and Scott, I've heard I'm "a gem," "the best" and "the best thing that's ever happened to me." Yet, I've never worn an "Engaged" or "Getting Married" button.

It was hard to drive out thoughts that I might be repeating the Rich pattern with Scott. His ruptured esophagus messed up more than his stomach. Along with taking out his spleen, the surgeon cut Scott's vagus nerve. This so-called superhighway nerve controls everything from our fight or flight instinct and digestion to emotional connection and expression via the brain's all-powerful, feel-good Oxytocin hormone. Once back on his feet, Scott wasn't in *nearly* the hurry he had been to create our life together. He couldn't work for more than a year, had colossal medical debt and had used up his savings by living on it during his year of recuperation. And, he was different emotionally. I had researched the impact of cutting the vagus nerve, and it didn't sound good for relationships. Yes, he assured me he still saw us married, still saw us raising a family; he just couldn't name dates. He had recently begun a new job and asked me to be patient with him. I'd heard this story before.

I felt naked with my lone "Honorary Citizen" button and an empty left ring finger. I was prepared for the onslaught of longing from seeing so many kids in one place. What I hadn't seen coming was how much a naked left ring finger made me want to cry.

I spent twenty minutes searching for the right hat in The Mad Hatter shop, as I'd left my straw sunhat in the car. It seemed every third rack in the store had ten versions of Princess Tiaras with wedding veils attached: baby-pink, baby-blue, pale yellow, neon green, candy-apple red and yes, traditional white. I resisted the urge to try one on. Shopping usually makes me feel better, but the veils had me going from bad to worse. I tried to tune into the KLUV radio station's "All Love, All The Time," and eventually emerged from the hat store with a reversible floppy canvas number —soft blue on one side and a brightly colored collage of orange-tinted Disney characters on the other. I chose to wear it with the soft blue to the outside. If I'd felt a little less like crying, I might have bought the fun top hat with carrot colored hair streaming off it in honor of Johnny Depp's Mad Hatter in the movie *Alice in Wonderland*. I was starting to feel like I was in a Tim Burton film, too, with all the conflicting emotions and a huge desire to just feel right-sized, OK and whole.

Lisa is a Disneyland expert, and I gladly relinquished my usual take-charge role to her. Since hearing my doctor say that I needed surgery, my neck had been stiff, my chest squeezed tight and my leg muscles engaged even when I was lounging. But standing in line for the "It's A Small World" ride I became conscious that something felt different in my body. Knowing Lisa and Carmen were taking care of me, I began to unwind into a state of relaxation. Stranger still, I was allowing this TLC outside of my healing circle. I consciously entered a state of gratitude each time Lisa pointed out the food stands and restaurants that had salads and vegetables rather than burgers and pizza.

The Enjoyment perspective returning, I remembered just how much I love rides! I love the Space Mountain ride! I love Pirates of the Caribbean! I love Star Tours! The thrilling start of a roller coaster taking off got my heart pounding; the air rushing across my face and tangling my hair felt cleansing. On Space Mountain I found myself acting like my ten-year-old self as I threw one arm high in the air with feet lifted from the floor of the car. I held onto the safety bar with a vise-like grip with my other hand to protect my right ovary from the anticipated twists, turns and curves.

Sauntering from ride to ride, in spite of telling myself I wouldn't, I peered into as many strollers as I could. A sleeping baby, dressed in a loose, long sleeve, white t-shirt with a white diaper peeking out of a white blanket, evoked angels singing on high. His big brother, about four years old, yammered about where he wanted to go next. His slightly older sister wore a pink tulle princess dress. Her tiny fingers examined the sequins, and she kept looking down at the puffy skirt and laughing gleefully as she tripped over nothing in particular.

"Don't pull at the sequins, you'll pull them all off," said her exasperated dad. Longing tightened around my chest and I was glad my wraparound sunglasses hid the tears welling in my eyes.

I took a deep breath and tried to focus on the wedding stuff Lisa and Carmen were talking about, but my mind kept drifting back to the many painful conversations with Rich about putting off having children. When we were around friends or family members who had children, I brought up the subject. When I turned thirty-eight, and he once again said he was in no position to take on that responsibility, I hissed with more venom than I knew I had, "And by the time you are fucking ready, it will be too fucking late."

"I know," he said, tears filling his eyes. "That's why I've been looking into fertility options. I found out that they could freeze a fertilized egg for years and then implant it into your uterus. They offer that for young women before they go through chemo or radiation."

"You've been researching?" I asked, softening like butter left in the sun.

"Yes. Cat, I know this is important to you and because it is important to you, it is important to me. I honestly don't know if having kids is an imperative for me. I'm exhausted from too many years of too little sleep and dealing with child-like musicians."

He had a point. In building recording studios in our various homes, and running a commercial recording studio, we'd been acting as de-facto parents, or at least like the cool uncle and aunt who didn't care if you put your feet up on the furniture but minded very much if you did drugs. I'd had many late-night conversations with slightly drunk young men pining for love but whose behavior was that of a bad boy bordering on abuser. I think they talked to me because I told them the truth—their behavior was not in alignment with their words. I also wasn't in awe of them or their big-deal record company advances.

After Rich shared his research with me, I made an appointment with Dr. K to check out freezing my fertilized eggs. She walked me through the process and the price tag. While the price tag was exorbitant, prohibitively so for us without help, the side effects of daily hormone shots over several weeks were s-c-a-r-y. I did research and read several stories of women who'd had similar fertility treatments for IVF and later were diagnosed with ovarian cancer, Gilda Radner being one of them. I spoke with a friend who had recently gone through an in-vitro procedure (there was a successful implanting of the embryo, but she subsequently miscarried). She confirmed what I'd read online in various articles—the headaches were staggering, the nausea overwhelming and the chances of successful delivery of a child (11.5% chance in women over 40) are much lower than the chances for successful implantation in the uterus.

I counted how many days a month I was already down for the count with migraines. I added those up then multiplied by twelve. One hundred and twenty days out of every three hundred and sixty-five days I was found prone, in a dark and silent room, praying for Excedrin Migraine and ice packs, or Tylenol 3, to take away the pain. I thought about being in that incapacitated state for at least two weeks without any pain diminishing drugs.

I remembered how sick birth control pills made me when I was on them, and that they actually triggered more migraines in me, despite relieving them for others.

I considered my history of ovarian cysts. Did I really want to pump my body full of hormones that were known to make your ovaries grow things as well as hopefully release a high volume of eggs?

I thought about the fact that I stopped eating meat and poultry because of the added hormones and antibiotics. (Antibiotics in general feed the Candida that always lives in a stomach.) I also thought about the fact that I refused to explore Botox injections even though they can alleviate migraine headaches in some people.

I had to acknowledge that I had long ago decided to listen to my body instead of just doing what felt good in the moment when it came to my health.

I spoke with my doctor about a month after the initial consultation, and she asked a simple question that made up my mind. "Are you willing to repeat the procedure multiple times?"

In spite of what my friend had shared with me, the over-the-top optimist in me hadn't given any thought to the fact that it might not work. Could I put my body through the ringer like that multiple times? Could I put myself through another round after a miscarriage? My stomach squeezed in that way it does when my body doesn't want to do something. I told my doctor I'd call her back.

I decided to believe with all my heart that when the time was right for Rich and me, we'd conceive out of our passionate love for each other and have our little "Rich Cat" baby.

Departing Disneyland's Adventureland, I was pulled from my reverie when a little boy around four years old went into what I call the full-tilt-boogie-Target-at-five-p.m.-toddler-meltdown. He kept pointing toward and screaming about a ride in Adventureland, while the rest of the family was trying to leave. The way he tugged at his mom's arm to pull her back reminded me of those body builder types tugging the chain with all their might to get a loaded 18-wheeler truck rolling. "Yep, not longing for that family scene," I thought.

Instead, I envisioned myself pushing a stroller with my own little angel in it. I imagined cradling her next to me while we whirled around on the Dumbo ride in one of the flying purple elephant cars. I knew what a warm little hand in mine would feel like. I looked into the faces of the moms, imagining what it would be like to be them. I witnessed the young moms and moms around my age ooh and ah right alongside their kids over Goofy and Minnie and Mickey, all the while snapping pictures with iPhones. A forty-something mom sneaked a few licks of her kid's ice cream cone before getting intentionally caught. A twenty-something mom held a wad of cotton candy just above her well-behaved kid's outstretched hands and dispensed it one bite at a time. Smart, I thought. One mom appeared unaware she had mustard dribbling down her chin from taking a bite of her kid's hot dog. I imagined myself doing these same things, even savoring the sweets and migraine-inducing nitrates and trans-fats in hot dogs!

Standing in line for Big Thunder Mountain Railroad I must have stared a little too long because the mom on her iPhone slowly raised her head and looked in my direction, as if she could feel my eyes on her. Her little boy was engrossed in his Gameboy or iTouch, or some hand-held device. Her eyes seemed to sigh before they narrowed and she stiffened her stand, as if to say, "Walk in my shoes, honey." I felt awful. I knew I was judging her because being at Disneyland provoked my longing to be there with a child of my own. Of course, in my mind I'd have been soaking it all up and not annoyed by anything. Fantasy is great, just not real. I looked directly into her eyes and smiled. She shifted her weight from one foot to the other and half-smiled back. She had the tight-lipped look of a defiant kid caught doing something wrong. I chanted "All Love, All the Time" in my head as I continued to beam at her. I'd like to say she put away her iPhone and began to interact with her son, but she didn't.

Like the old political directive, "Vote early and vote often!" my Enjoyment perspective helped me outvote the sad mama-wanna-be inside. It helped me outvote the emptiness I felt when I looked at my unadorned left ring finger. It helped me outvote the niggling little "what if . . . ." around my health and fertility.

The big turning point came when I bought a souvenir—an almost hot-pink Tinkerbelle t-shirt. She sits crossed legged in a lotus yoga posture, with my favorite kind of affirmations surrounding her. "Unlock the Secrets of Illumination" and "Let your Spirit Fly" floated above her head; Her left wing said "A Magic" and her right wing "From Within"; "Follow Your Inner Light" and "Believe in Who You Are" hug her from each side, and below her figure, in perfect lotus petals—"Free to Be Original, Free to be Happy, Free to be Yourself." The phrase "Free to be the Best You Can Be" under all the images seems to anchor Tink and her magic producing thoughts. I decided to live into Tinkerbelle and whispered to her, "Yes, I believe. I believe. I believe!"

CHAPTER 13

The Almost
Seven-Year-Itch

1997 was no different than any other year filled with a few big "firsts" of their kind. Madeline Albright became the first woman Secretary of State for the U.S. and IBM's Deep Blue chess-playing computer beat the human world chess champion, Garry Kasparov.

There were some big endings, too. Princess Diana was killed in a horrible car crash and Hong Kong returned to Chinese rule from the UK.

Some of these events involved lengthy and detailed planning, but even the surprise death of Princess Diana was rife with clues leading up to it. It has been reported that she and Dodi Fayed were terrified for their lives when it came to the insatiable hounding of the Paparazzi. Yet most of us, celebrities or otherwise, don't pay attention to clues. We are too consumed by the responsibilities of making a living and taking care of those we love. That is, we aren't aware of the clues until something big happens, and we look back to see just how we arrived in our new circumstance, facing new choices, or no choices at all because we look too late.

Rich and I lived the life of two ambitious people both out to make the world a better place. He worked tirelessly (and a little harder than I thought was good for him) to bring about change in the music business. Running commercial recording studios in North Hollywood and in Mammoth, CA, while creating temporary studios in mansions all over Los Angeles, he built relationships with top-selling artists, some of whom became good friends. Because the work also involved endlessly trying to please petulant, selfish boy-men with big record advances (who in general believe their press clippings and didn't think their genius needed to give anyone else credit for brilliant songs), Rich grew weary. He also drove the six hours back and forth from North Hollywood to Mammoth about every two weeks. I flew up or drove up to be there on alternate weekends. While Rich was in Mammoth, I tended to the local studios, making sure the staff had everything they needed like a well-stocked fridge, petty cash and supplies for recording. This sort of pitching in came alongside of my growing coaching, speaking and workshop business. I was also on the board of directors of one of the first professional associations for coaches and I'd taken on the role of conference chair, falling back on my experience as an event planner for Los Angeles Party Designs. My business brought in monthly sustenance and his brought the wild ride common in the entertainment business; big paydays with lag time between them.

At the beginning of 1997, it became clear that we could no longer sustain all the recording studios. One after the next, they became casualties of the shift in the music industry. Twenty-four track tape machines, the size of vending machines, along with soundproofed live recording rooms, were being replaced with digital recording and computer editing. Rich's studios had been filled with high-end and vintage gear, some of it used by the likes of The Beatles. Rich and his gear recorded what turned out to be a 1990's backdrop of top-ten hits and gold records. The good news was Rich's clients all believed in his expertise and many asked him to build computer-based recording rigs in road cases they could take on tour with them.

After closing the Mammoth property studio, all of a sudden, Rich was home almost all the time. Keith, Rich's go-to-guy, wound up living for a few months in our small two-bedroom apartment in Burbank after the North Hollywood studio (and his living space) was shuttered. Instead of shopping weekly for the studio, I was now feeding three of us every night at home, rather than eating out, which Rich and I had become accustomed to doing when traveling back and forth to Mammoth.

We learned to coordinate our schedules each week. I'd lay out when my coaching calls were so Keith would know when to head to the little office Rich had kept around the corner from the studio, and Rich would know when to take the dogs to the park. He made calls from there before going to the small office. Thank goodness Keith decided to stay on with Rich. Ten years younger, he knew how to record music on a computer. In that little office, they designed and built those travel recording gear rigs Rich's clients wanted. We "made it work" but I was stepping over the obvious—it wasn't working for me.

I could hang with an extra person in our apartment. I actually enjoyed cooking for and feeding people. I loved both of our dogs madly. What didn't work were our unstable finances. All the specialized studio gear was expensive and we were up to our eyeballs financing it with less frequent big paydays. The fact that the equipment wasn't being used any more didn't mean the loans disappeared. We were sliding into a precarious situation.

I got busy doing what I do from habit—rescue and help. I leveraged my credit, took big chunks of money that came my way and gave them to Rich instead of investing back in my business. I slid down the rabbit hole of sacrifice. The big problem with this particular rabbit hole is it becomes polluted with expectation, which morphs into disappointment and then into resentment pretty quickly. Hello Suck It Up Buttercup mask. I believed that if I could keep us together through this hardship and help Rich get what he wanted; I would get the family I wanted.

Yet I was itchy. I was itchy to be out from under the burden of mounting debt. I had not grown up that way, my parents paying off credit cards each month, so I tried to understand what "lesson" I was supposed to learn. I wrote in my journal daily to find some clues. I meditated and prayed for a way forward. I looked at filing bankruptcy, and when I mentioned that to Rich, the combination of his crushed look and his question, "You don't believe in me anymore?" was more than I could bear. I didn't follow through with the attorney even though I knew I was spinning out of control in a very unfamiliar world with no roadmap to guide me.

So when Tim, a man I met at a professional conference earlier that year, who had built and sold a lucrative business and already made his mark in the world, started flirting with me at a subsequent conference, I flirted back in spite of my best efforts not to. He had wowed me during his presentation at the first conference. He had kept in touch after the first conference, offering to help me build my business, help me coordinate a program I was working on, and sometimes called to read me an uplifting quote. In those conversations I'd asked him questions about ambitious men, as he was one. I'd shared with him about my desire for children and Rich's delays. One day when Rich came home he heard me laughing and I froze. Why was I laughing with Tim like this? Rich asked me "why does this guy call so often?" and warned me that Tim wanted something from me. I said he didn't, and was just a friend.

I couldn't remember the last time Rich and I had flirted with and been utterly charmed by each other. With someone living in our space, even our passion was anemic. From the way Tim looked at me at that second conference, I knew I was over the line. I stopped flirting and reminded Tim I was in a committed relationship. Tim changed tactics. He began to say things to me, like I was special. He told me I was luscious. He told me he wanted to make my dreams of family come true. I tried to avoid him. It seemed impossible to love Rich so much yet be attracted to someone else. Was I attracted to Tim or his word pictures? It seemed impossible to know my flirting was wrong and keep doing it. We kissed the last night of the conference, and I felt like I wore the Scarlet A on my shoulder the next day. My stomach became a juicer, and I couldn't keep anything inside me. Rich knew, even before he picked me up at the airport. I had not answered my hotel phone when he rang just past midnight. Rich and I were psycho-spiritually connected from the moment we met. I knew when something was happening to him, good or bad, no matter how far away he physically was from me. He could feel what was happening with me, too.

He picked me up from my late-night flight into LAX on that Sunday night, and we walked around and around and around our neighborhood with the dogs because Keith was asleep on the living room couch. I didn't want to hurt Rich, so I hemmed and hawed before telling him everything. We both knew those kisses were about much more.

No matter how much I loved Rich, I yearned for our life to be easier, simpler. I yearned for financial stability. I yearned for him to stop pushing us to our edges all the time. He yearned for more time to "make it right" financially and take care of me like he'd always wanted to. He yearned for me to believe in him again. He yearned for a fresh start for us. We grappled with the betrayals until 3:00 in the morning—my kissing another man and him breaking his promises around finances and giving me what I wanted—a child. He looked at me, tears running from those eyes I lose myself in and said, "I am a jealous man, but I am bigger than this. *We* are bigger than all of this."

I reiterated that Tim was a symptom, not my fix. But Rich wanted me to be sure. So I spent a few days and nights at Veronica's to sort through my emotions and give Rich and me some space we didn't have with Keith on the couch. I wrote about my conflicting feelings in my journal. Tim called daily and reiterated that he'd never met anyone like me, wanted to be with me and invited me to visit him. He was used to closing deals and was very persuasive. As excited as Tim's words made me, I missed being in Rich's arms and left Veronica's. He missed me, too, but could feel my inner turmoil so he put me on a plane early one fall Saturday morning to meet up with Tim in a neutral space (as in, not his home city either). "We have to be clear if we are moving forward and if we are moving forward, there can be no one else in this relationship," Rich said before I boarded the plane. I nodded my head in agreement. He said he would pick me up at the airport that night. Tim and I met at The Hotel del Coronado in San Diego.

Yes, I was still attracted to him. Yes, I was curious about what it might be like to jump into a relationship with him. Yes, I wanted to hear all he had to say about how he saw us getting married, having children (he already had a child from his first marriage) and living happily ever after. The fast-moving Aries in me was excited, but felt his speed was dizzying. As alluring as he was and his fantasy of a happy married life, there was something missing for me. As I gazed at him in the late afternoon beach sun, I recognized what was missing. Building a relationship—he leapt from the starting line to the winner's circle. And, most of all, he wasn't Rich, and I was still in love with Rich.

It felt a little like the end of *Casablanca* when Tim took me back to the San Diego airport that night. I boarded the small twin-engine prop plane via the tarmac and looked back at him before walking up the stairs. We were both crying, and we both knew I was making the right choice to get on that plane and fly back to Rich. The Cat and Rich story was not done.

Rich, a true romantic had two long stemmed roses with him when he picked me up. One was yellow for friendship, the other red for passion. He asked me which it would be. I said both and threw my arms around his neck, my body melting into the comfort of his familiarity and the physical compatibility of us.

We decided to hit the reset button. We decided to leave our past mistakes and hurts on one side of the line as we stepped into a new, fresh start. We began by going to one of our favorite falling-in-love-days Italian restaurants, exuding the curiosity of a first date. Then we went to a favorite club and danced all night. We dated again—we didn't just grab dinner. We decided we were in it, this thing called life, together.

Keith moved out, finances were still tight, but Rich and I believed in what the other was doing. We marched onward into 1998 and kept going. The feast or famine finances continued to be an issue. I still wanted to start our family yesterday.

Reset buttons only reset, they don't necessarily perform an upgrade.

CHAPTER 14

Fast Intimacy

The woman I called Grandmommy, my maternal grandmother, had open-heart surgery when she was eighty-six. She was hospitalized again when she fractured her pelvis and shoulder just before her ninety-fourth birthday. Both times, she became the hospital staff's favorite patient. No matter how awful the news from a doctor or how much a nurse's blood draw hurt she'd gift them with her smile and impish charm, "Thank yew so much, precious. Thank yeeeww!" They knew she meant it.

I make up that her smile helped get her loved ones through the lean years of the dust bowl, the Great Depression, and WWII. The third of eight siblings, she was born in 1909 and raised on the harsh land of central Texas, in a farmhouse with no electricity or indoor plumbing. While the land is beautiful, it was hard, as a farmer, to make a predictable living out of it. Some years there was adequate rain, other years too much, and many years, not enough rain to keep the grass growing for livestock, much less bring a crop of cotton to maturity.

"Well, of course I picked cotton as a child, honey. We all did," she'd laugh, demonstrating her delicate technique with her small hands, which resembled doing fine needlework like lacework or embroidery. "You had to pull it from the pod just so or the sharp points of the pod would cut you." Her tone changed from lighthearted reminiscence to a warning. "The last thing you wanted to do was bleed onto that cotton." There was punishment for such a careless, bloody offense to a crop that had to feed ten people for a year.

She wept every time she spoke of Winnie, her adored older sister who died from complications of a high fever. "Nobody could figure out where Sister contracted the illness because none of the rest of us got sick. Papa let me look in the window at Winnie before she died, but only Mama and he could go in. I never got to say goodbye." She'd pull out a Kleenex from her cardigan or skirt pocket and dab at her tears. All cardigans, blouses and skirts had to have pockets for Kleenex or she wouldn't wear them.

The older my grandmother got the more important the stories of her youth and early marriage became to her. She delighted in telling about her one-room-schoolhouse teaching days in the Texas panhandle. My favorite story is how my grandfather, then her suitor, secretly lit the wood stove in that little schoolhouse on blustery winter mornings so it would be toasty warm when she and the students arrived. "I finally got there early enough one morning to see him dash out the door and jump on his horse. I thanked him at church that Sunday!" They were married shortly after her second year of teaching.

Even in her nineties, whenever my grandmother smiled, she conjured up the playful, optimistic, beautiful young woman in her high school graduation picture. She drops her chin down just a bit and tilts her head to the left ever so slightly and looks up at you. Her chocolate brown eyes gleam with infectious enthusiasm. I think her grin makes her look like she knows that the secret to life is love. And love is what I experienced and saw pour over people from that smile of hers.

In grocery lines, airplanes and waiting rooms, my extroverted grandmother and I share an inclination to talk to strangers about things that matter. My shy, introverted mom remains perplexed by this, *especially* in a doctor's office waiting room. As soon as my mom settles in her chair, she opens her purse and whips out a book of crossword puzzles or a magazine. Before arthritis set in and a second carpal tunnel surgery, she always had embroidery with her. I remember reading my Nancy Drew books sitting next to her as she embroidered, waiting at the orthodontist's office or in the car for my brother to come out of the Jr. High locker room, red-faced from football practice.

After her mother's heart surgery, my mom would drive 90 miles from Port Arthur to Houston to accompany my grandmother to follow-up appointments. She thought my grandmother took too many things said by a doctor at face value and didn't ask enough questions. To be fair, in the six-month long siege leading up to my father's death, Mom and I learned to ask the hard questions and to be sure that we understood what was being said.

"Your grandmother did it again!" she exclaimed over the phone after one of those doctor visits with my grandmother.

"What has she riled you with this time?" I asked jokingly, knowing it would be one of three things. 1. My grandmother had spoken to strangers. 2. She had walked through the grocery store again, her purse dangling open on her delicate wrist. 3. She and my mom had gotten into their ongoing, forty-year religious debate.

Fortunately, it wasn't the religion thing, though I have to hand it to my grandmother for her ceaseless optimism that one day she'd convince someone else in the family that her non-denominational minister wasn't nuts. He liked to be called Colonel, wore his military uniform to "preach," and dissected Bible verses on an overhead projector while his "students" took copious notes, as if preparing for a final exam. Though there was no pipe organ playing uplifting spirituals, my grandmother and her friends somehow seemed to receive a high from the experience.

"Your grandmother sat right next to a woman about her age and before I even got out my crossword puzzle, they were talking in detail about every ailment they had."

I could imagine the scene. My grandmother sits down, smiles, and the woman next to her, utterly charmed, smiles back. They soak in each other's smiles and their exchange of pleasantries quickly turns into medical history and the loss of their husbands, at which point both women reach for Kleenex in a pocket or blouse sleeve. When the other woman is called to enter the exam room, my grandmother squeezes her hands and with fondness says, "Really nice talking with you." A phrase my grandmother always meant.

"Mom, why does this disturb you so?"

"I guess I'm just weary of medical talk. I don't want to hear about stranger's woes." I think of those six months of hell she spent every day with my father in the ICU before he died. I understand my mom. She is still weary with grief from his death, and the grief of watching her own father die of a heart attack in front of her in the kitchen three short years later while Grandmommy was in the hospital. Yet, my mom remains the go to medical handler for the family. It's more worry than she can hold, but hold it she does. I'm the opposite of my mom. I find comfort in talking with people about harrowing experiences, especially around hospitals – hearing theirs and sharing mine.

My grandmother triumphed over cancer in her mid-seventies via traditional chemo. I was thinking about this when Dr. S, the naturopathic doctor I had been referred to, called. It was early Friday afternoon, and I was driving south on the Pacific Coast Highway through Malibu to get to Santa Monica. I was scheduled for a hair appointment before dinner with new networking buddies. I'd met them the week prior at my favorite monthly professional association event.

I'd been asked onto the stage by the speaker to participate in an exercise. He was a short man with snow-white hair, who bore a new management book and an old-boys-club feel. In trying to demonstrate his point, he wound up insulting me, asking the audience, "Isn't she pretty?" as he leered at my tailored suit-clad body. I was being sexually harassed, in front of my peers. My Aries anger rose, ready to scorch a hole in the earth big enough to bury him in. I knew I had a choice to make quickly deciding it wasn't worth exploding at him in front of almost one hundred colleagues and potential clients. Instead, commenting and questioning at the same time in that decidedly cool and detached way of a 1940's movie star, I said, "Exactly what is your point?"

After the rest of the tiresome presentation, many colleagues circled around me to share their outrage while several board members apologized for the speaker's behavior. My new buddies became my new buddies, however, when they congratulated me on how I handled the situation with grace and grit. I had already met Bev at a prior monthly event, and she introduced me to Liz who said, "I love that you didn't have to yell or put him down to put him in his place." We agreed that we wanted to get together and talk about coaching women and how we might support each other. I schedule multiple appointments or activities in the L.A. area when one pops up, so I was doubling up with a hair appointment and networking fun.

Answering the phone, I heard a voice like fine, soft silk, and immediately felt at ease with Dr. S, even as she asked me questions about my digestion and poop. My mom says I wear my heart on my sleeve. I suppose that's true since I tear up at commercials and any National Anthem being played as an athlete receives a gold medal. And almost always when I talk about someone I love. Sure enough, my tears flowed as Dr. S's warm voice assured me she thought a naturopathic approach could work for me. She said all dis-ease (pronouncing it as two words) is a result of an out of balance system. Her approach would address the underlying imbalance, rather than the symptoms. "Ovarian growths are generally about imbalance," she said. I thought about what my holistic MD told me in 1991—that good health is achieved through a balance of good bacteria in the gut, nutrients in the cells, and emotions in our lives.

To myself I said, "Take two, Cat!" And was surprised and grateful when she offered to speak with me that Sunday afternoon, since her next week was already booked solid. "Thank you so much! Thank you! Thank you! Thank you!"

When I got off the phone with Dr. S, I made a mental gratitude list of all the serendipitous events that had transpired in the past ten days and then turned my attention to getting my hair highlighted and cut.

There is something marvelous about having someone touch your head! It opens you up. In fact, I believe it would be an excellent tactic for police detectives to use on suspects. The LAPD should install salon hair-washing sinks in all interview rooms and have trained hair washers on staff to shampoo and condition suspects' hair! If we lulled suspects into the zone that everyone reaches at a hair salon, confessions would spill out just like life stories do with our "hair-a-pist" every month or two.

Lynne's hair studio is in her townhome. The front door is flanked by giant Fu Dogs and I can't help but run my fingers over their smooth ceramic heads before I knock on her door. After a quick hug, she offers tea, water, snacks or whatever else you may need. The vibe is Hawaiian lanai mixed with urban style and old-world Japanese antiques. An enormous cement Buddha head sits on the low credenza next to the patio door that opens to an intimate covered gazebo with a daybed, cozy chairs and large fountain. An art project of some sort was usually laid out on the counter-height dark brown bamboo dining room table, and today was no different. "I've started making jewelry! I took a bead class and am hooked," she said as I looked at the stacked Lucite organizers holding thousands of beads in different colors, sizes and shapes, and noticed the half-finished bracelet and necklace.

Lynne has been my stylist for three years. The first time I sat in her chair, Rich and I were in the middle of dissolving our seventeen-year relationship, and trying to do it in as loving, and generous a way possible to pave the way for life-long friendship. I could hardly look in the giant mirror in front of me that summer day because I looked so skinny and tired. I found myself wishing I'd worn under eye concealer when I saw the enormous dark circles staring back at me.

Now as I settled into a chair and sipped freshly steeped green tea, she mixed hair color and asked, "What's new?" And as in the days of my breakup with Rich, I knew she really wanted to hear my answer.

She foil-packaged my hair with highlights and lowlights as I told her about the last week's worth of shock and fear, the healing circle, and taking charge of when I'd have the surgery. I also said I'd been to Disneyland. "Holy crap, I can't believe it has only been a little more than a week. It feels like years," I said.

I looked at Lynne standing behind me in the mirror gauging her reaction. "I think you can heal the growth without surgery. I had a similar thing happen a few years ago. I never found out what it was, and I don't really care to. It went away and hasn't come back," she said. I love when the Universe sends a confirmation of my exact thinking. I knew I was well on my way to not needing surgery after the healing circle with my goddess sisters.

Lynne retreated into her bedroom, calling out, "I still have the crystal someone gave me during that time." She returned holding a quartz and earthy red combo crystal. It had a long black cord attached to it so it could be worn as a necklace. "I have no idea what it is, but it's supposed to help balance female organs. I would lie in bed and massage my whole lower torso with it and wear it during the day." She offered it up and said, "It's yours now, take it."

It felt heavier in my hand than I expected. Crystals are deceptive in that they look so light. While my hair processed, we thumbed through a few of Lynne's books on the healing powers of crystals. I couldn't find what that earthy red part of this combo crystal was and decided to trust I was not supposed to know.

After Lynne's million-dollar hair touch and some primping, I drove to the restaurant to meet my new friends. In trying to find a time we could all meet I revealed that I was dealing with a medical thing, so they already knew there was something going on with my body. "Don't let this overtake the whole evening, Cat," I said aloud as I parked my car.

CHAPTER 15

Sharing
Our Stories

I arrived first at the Italian restaurant. Surveying all the open tables, I tried not to grin when I told the host I had a reservation. Assuring me in haughty Italian-accented English that every table would be taken before long, he escorted me to a prime table next to the window along Wilshire Boulevard.

While I waited for my dinner companions to arrive, I thought back to my WRS networking days, connecting the dots I couldn't make sense of the morning Dr. K told me I needed surgery. Through WRS I made lasting friendships, supported other women as a coach and got to support others via referrals to their business. I also found two caring and relationship-driven women doctors, win-win-win-win.

At the very first Women's Referral Service networking meeting I attended in 1994, I was still in the acting world, though in training to become a professional life coach, or more precisely, one of the first six certified professional coaches in the United States. An actress friend I'd met through Women In Theater, who was also a distributor for a high-end costume jewelry company, invited me to come to a networking luncheon as her guest. When she introduced me, I stood up and said with a pride that surprised me, "I am Cat Williford, and I'm a professional life coach!" I saw the cocked heads, raised eyebrows and thought bubbles that read, "Huh? What's that?" So I smiled and continued: "You know how a personal trainer at the gym helps you set body goals and navigate the equipment? Well, I help you set life and business goals and navigate the obstacles." The raised eyebrows shifted to smiles and the cocked heads straightened. I left the luncheon with two new clients. Telling people I was an actress all those years never elicited that much engagement.

I can't help but smile at all the fun I had while networking. Getting clients by talking with people about what matters in life was so much better than auditioning for creeps who asked, "Can you dumb her down?" or, "Do you do nudity?" My answers, "No, I can't," and "No," to their stupid, dull questions became tiresome. When one particularly smarmy producer asked, "Sweetie, can you dumb her down?" I snapped. "As a matter of fact, I can't. I'm fairly certain that she and I both have a higher IQ than you do." I may have even mentioned that I had graduated on the Dean's List from Stephens College. I grabbed my bag and slammed the door behind me, later calling my agent and manager to let them know there would definitely not be a callback.

I joke that I stopped attending networking meetings because of the underdone chicken dinners. The truth is I approached net-working like I approach most things: with zeal enough for two people and therefore burned out after five years. In that zeal I built up my coaching practice to a word-of-mouth-referral business, became a keynote speaker, workshop leader, and trainer of other coaches and founded The Modern Goddess. TMG began as a four-part workshop, teaching women to own all parts of their feminine energy. It developed into more workshops, retreats, a Spiritual way of life, my circle of goddess-sister-friends and my distinct way of coaching women. The conclusion of the first workshop was a full moon ceremony—something I'd never done before though it felt like I'd been leading them all my life (or lives!).

The commotion of the restaurant door opening and closing jostled me from my memories, and I saw that Bev had arrived. She spotted me instantly as only one other table of diners had appeared in between our arrivals. Bev wore a subtle patterned scarf of muted autumn colors draped just so around her shoulders. "Smart," I thought, "everything about Bev is smart." I made the mental note to begin playing with scarves again. I have a combination of classic, yet feminine styled clothing with eclectic pieces to mix in. Lately, I'd indulged my love of animal print anything (purses, blouses, shoes) and was feeling very playful in my wardrobe.

Bev sat directly across from me and we chatted about the merits of living on the Westside of L.A. rather than the valley, where we'd both lived for many years. "I'm a born and bred valley girl," she laughed, sounding more like a native New Yorker. The restaurant filled up as we dove into conversation about how we both got to be living where we were now: breakups.

"What happened?" I asked, wanting to join her in tearing the warm, fragrant bread into bite-sized chunks before dipping them in the garlic-seasoned olive oil. But I knew better after a gastroenterologist who had read my test results said, "I'd never eat gluten again if I were you." If I hadn't felt so much better without it, I might have been even more tempted to indulge.

"We were really young. I married my college sweetheart and had kids fast." She shared that in hindsight, they'd probably gotten married too young though she'd never, ever be sorry since she cherishes her two children. "It was an amicable split, though not without its share of heartache." Her voice broke a little when she revealed how quickly her husband re-coupled. "Years later, we're all friends," she said sincerely.

I thought about my college sweetheart, Rob. I arrived in Columbia, MO in 1984 at Stephens College after two years at the University of Texas. Though Stephens is a woman's college, the University of Missouri (MU) is just a few blocks away. I'd wound up at Stephens after my mom, also a Stephens graduate, enrolled me in a summer theatre program there. I loved the intimate class size and old world charm of the campus dating back to 1833. The theatre department at UT was huge, and I was frustrated by the lack of personal attention. I wondered how in the heck I would ever develop my talent with only two reviews of my work each semester. My "freshman ten" had doubled my sophomore year, and my mom knew I was not happy. For my sophomore spring break, I'd convinced my parents to take me to NYC—I was done with school and just wanted to get on with giving professional acting a go. We met with a roommate finder service to explore housing options and I picked up Backstage magazine to check out audition opportunities. We went to see the hits of the year, *A Chorus Line*, *Brighten Beach Memoirs* and *Noises Off*. My father was starting to soften a little on the thought of me moving to NYC until the last day we were there and my mom was mugged. Good-bye big city dreams, at least for a little while, I thought. (Mom was not injured in the mugging, thank God.)

Rob was a grad student at MU. We met spring of my junior year when he and I were cast in an extra-curricular one-act play series put on by the senior directing class students. We hit it off right away and dated the rest of the semester, stayed in touch over the summer and picked back up my senior year. We were in love, and we both had dreams—he of being a news anchor, me of a professional career in acting. During the last semester of my senior year it became clear to me, he wasn't as interested in leaving Missouri as I had thought he was. And I was definitely not interested in staying in Missouri, especially after being accepted into The Neighborhood Playhouse in NYC for graduate school. But when push came to shove, at my parents' house the summer after graduation, I recognized how tired of being in school I was. (I had not had a summer off since just after my senior year of high school. I'd attended summer school at UT after my freshman year, the summer theatre program my mom enrolled me in after my sophomore year, and then worked in Stephen's summer stock theatre between my junior and senior years.) I was even more tired of being cold in the winter. A theatre classmate at Stephens was from L.A. and had moved back after graduation. As we chatted one day it became clear I wanted to move to California. She found us an apartment in Hollywood and I packed up my car! Rob flew to Houston and helped me drive from the Gulf Coast of Texas to L.A. We fooled ourselves for a while thinking we could be a long-distance couple. He had one more year of grad school left, and I was pushing him to consider broadcast journalism in Los Angeles. He was really good on air as an anchor and as a reporter. I figured landing a job couldn't be that hard, even in such a big market, could it?

I was supposed to fly to Missouri for Thanksgiving, but starting in late October, I could hear distance in his voice. His stories seemed to revolve around one of his female friends (whom I knew was sweet on him all along and didn't seem to like me very much). The week before I was due to visit, he said it wouldn't be a good idea for me to fly to St. Louis. I asked if his mom, who had Parkinson's, had taken a turn for the worse. He said yes, and then admitted that he and Laura had been hanging out. Turns out, a long distance relationship wasn't for him. I was heartbroken, furious and relieved, all at the same time. Here I was new to L.A. and finding it hard not to date all the cute guys I was meeting. Even though I sobbed for a week and felt rejected, my ending with Rob didn't belong in the same sentence with my heartache with Rich.

Bev and I talked about the after-effects of life shattering break-ups . . . like how we both felt shitty about ourselves, wondering what we could have done differently. She wanted to know if it was possible to feel the wonder of falling in love again, like the first time. I told her yes. I'd felt that with Scott. I wondered if it was normal to curl up on the floor in a fetal position and sob every night for several months as I had when Rich and I unwound our life together. She smiled and laughed with recognition. "I did that, too, so it must be normal since we both did it!"

I was grateful that my new friend is someone who talks about real things. I come alive in conversations about life and the heart. "I feel like I've known you for years!" I said, sipping the last bit of froth from my cappuccino. She nodded and said, "I know, I know!"

Just then Liz arrived. And though she was late it seemed like perfect timing in my conversation with Bev.

"I live the closest to this restaurant of the three of us, and I arrived last! Go figure! I always think I can do that one last thing. I totally miscalculated Friday night traffic!"

She took off her gloves and loosened her simple black wool scarf, letting it enfold her tailored jacket as she spoke. I noticed we both wore cashmere turtle-necked sweaters under our jackets. The neck of mine felt too tight suddenly and I wished I'd tried on the darn thing before buying it. I pulled on the neck to stretch it, not caring if I created a permanent change.

Liz initiated our professional conversation. "What types of clients are you looking for?" she asked. I nodded to Bev to go first. I suppose if you put any three coaches together at a table, the discussion will turn toward goals, dreams and big picture "bucket list" things. We were no different. As Liz talked about the book she was writing on coaching in the nursing profession, I felt a wave of knowing, as if I'd known her for lifetimes. And then, the conversation effortlessly veered from the professional into the personal.

"What's your greatest concern about the surgery?" Liz asked before taking a bite of her salmon.

"Losing the last shred of my fertility," I said, tearing up and leaning back in my chair. "In addition to my FSH test numbers indicating low chances of pregnancy, there is the possibility of the ovary being removed during surgery. Plus, in researching the procedure online, I read that anesthesia can mess with hormones." Liz reached for my hand and neither of us said anything for a moment.

"A woman's choices are not easy," Liz said.

"I didn't make conscious choices about marriage or kids. I just did what I thought I was supposed to," said Bev between bites of her Salad Nicoise.

145

"Me, too. But now I'm making choices—choices that have brought me to L.A. while my family remains in Idaho," said Liz, pausing before continuing, "I do miss my kids, but it is good for their father to have to do some hands-on parenting. And it is good for them." She paused and grinned before finishing her thought, "And it is really good for me." Liz had come to L.A. to train nurses in her coaching program and one gig led to another. She also discovered the mental space to actually write her book here, she said. She alluded to the space being good for her marriage as well.

I felt a twinge, a kick, a bubble; a something in my right ovary area as I swallowed a bite of salmon swirled in mashed potatoes. I put my fork down. What just happened in there, I asked myself. Immediately the word "healing" went through my mind. Yes, intimacy is healing I thought.

My grandmother connected at a heart level with strangers in doctors' waiting rooms. It was her brand of wisdom. My own wisdom had brought me into intimacy with these two women in the tumult of life on a brisk Friday night in March. My wisdom had led me to call a healing circle for myself, and invite beloved friends to infuse my body and Spirit with healing energy.

Returning to the table after a quick visit to the Ladies' room, I saw an energetic "bubble" around our table—a wispy, gossamer thin pinkish atmosphere. Liz and Bev leaned in and really looked into each other's eyes as they spoke. I'd experienced the same kind of soul-seeing energy all night. To an outsider, the three of us probably looked like long time friends.

Just before we parted, Liz held my hand while looking me squarely in the eyes and said, "You are going to be all right." I believed her. I believed her because she is an RN; I believed her because she seemed to be channeling some ethereal news source; and I believed her because I wanted to.

Driving home, my mind wandered through the events of the past week. What was it all pointing me toward, I wondered? "Belief" was the quick answer.

What do I believe in, I wondered? I believe in wisdom. I believe in the body's ability to heal itself with proper support and re-balancing. I believe in gratitude. I believe in kindness. I believe in strong eye contact. I believe in optimism and even cock-eyed optimism. I believe in miracles. And, I believe in the power and magic of intimacy, whether in a doctor's waiting room, healing circle, or over an Italian dinner in a restaurant that did, indeed, fill up with people and life.

CHAPTER 16

Seeing is Believing

Nestling into my happy looking sofa, my back facing the direction recommended by feng shui for meditation and spiritual connection, I hold my arms in front of me as if cradling my infant. I imagine a delicate, crocheted yellow cap on a teeny head and feel the weight of the tiny body nestled in my arms. A sunburst of warmth is quickly followed by a tingling sensation that flows from my heart as I caress his soft cheek. Sometimes I sense a son, other times I sense a daughter. I smell the freshness of new life as I hold my bundle of joy. "I promise I will do my very best as your mama. Thank you for coming into my life, and thank you for waiting for me. I know our timing is perfect!" The vision feels more real each time. The deeper I am immersed in it, the more tissues I use to wipe my tears and blow my nose.

The movie and subsequent book *The Secret* and almost anything from Wayne Dyer, have turned a vast number of New Agers into visioning enthusiasts. I mean no disrespect. I make annual vision boards, and even coach others to do the same after taking them through a guided visualization. And yet, I believe we have all been visioning via daydreaming our whole lives.

Some days, I access visioning consciously, like when I imagine holding my baby to be. I've also envisioned how I want meetings to go, the successful delivery of workshops, keynote addresses and seminars. When I've strayed from healthy routines, I visualized the impact of eating well and exercising, right down to a pleasing number on the scale.

Other days, the visualizing happens spontaneously, as when I slip into a daydream. I'm not consciously trying to conjure up some future reality; it's just that my mind has naturally drifted in that direction. Then there are the *Nightmare on Elm Street* scenarios that can take over my thoughts when I am feeling scared, lonely or angry.

Emotional times are stressful because they invite in the gremlins and saboteurs: the parts of me that demand I play it safe and stick to the rules. Conversely, other parts of me envision scenarios where I blow up the norm, storm out, make a scene. When I feel like nobody cares, I might imagine a scenario where everyone is really sorry they weren't nicer to me as they mourn me graveside. Really, I've done this!

In 1991, when every ounce of my experience and working knowledge of the medical universe was Western medicine, and yet the antibiotics weren't working, I began to envision getting sicker and sicker, being bedridden, even dying. I noticed that each time I lost control of my thoughts or daydreams, as I called them then, I felt worse within hours. The diarrhea kicked in, my throat seemed to fill with what felt like ground glass, and my fever spiked.

An actress, I had been trained to fantasize about a character's backstory. With this in mind, I decided to create a positive health story. I imagined working with my alternative doctor as if I were a character in a play who had just undergone an intense Candida cleanse. I envisioned my throat full of healthy-looking tissue and telling my doctor that I had not experienced one sore throat or episode of diarrhea in weeks. I imagined myself eating something forbidden, like cake and ice cream, and still feeling great the next day. I even envisioned my stomach full of healthy bacteria that resembled the happy little dancing cells with smiley faces I remembered from a sixth grade science movie.

These envisioning tactics are the same ones I use with clients stuck in the loop of a disempowering old or borrowed story. I ask them to imagine what the gremlins (those inner beings who constantly criticize us) look like. Most describe a sneaky, ugly troll, a giant, hairy, scary monster or some version of a bully. Then we make a list of all the nasty, recriminating, blaming, shaming, guilt-inducing, crappy things gremlins say, like, "Who do you think you are to (fill in the blank)," and "You can't do that! What will people think?" and "You aren't (fill in the blank) enough," and "Why bother? You won't succeed." Underneath each taunt or slur is the feeling: "I'm not good enough." I swear, if I could invent a magic machine it would look like an old red phone booth from England and when someone stepped inside it, gremlin-induced fears that make us feel small and inadequate would instantly be removed. Simultaneously this magic machine would open up a whoop-ass can of self-love, self-acceptance, and confidence.

Daily, I leveraged all my powers of positive, intentional visioning to overcome the "what ifs" and fear surrounding the tissue-filled growth. As I waited for Dr. S's call, I envisioned my right ovary surrounded by an amethyst purple, healing energy-infused sparkly light. I envisioned the growth diminishing and vanishing with a pouf, leaving my ovary healthy and whole.

CHAPTER 17

Leftovers

Though expected, the call from Dr. S startled me. "Any divine beings floating around my living room, please bless this conversation for my highest good, and the highest good of all." I spoke my failsafe prayer to remind me that I didn't want my Chief Operating Officer of Control mask to dominate.

"Hello, Cat." The sound of Dr. S's silky voice allowed me to surrender further. After a bit of chitchat she said, "I got your list of supplements, thank you."

"I hope the way I laid it out makes sense," I said, thinking about the detailed list I had sent that included strength, frequency and brand.

"It's perfect. Is there anything you need from me to ensure this is a safe space?" Dr. S asked. I smiled, recognizing the coaching question.

I paused to consider. After a moment I stated, "I need to name that I have a smidgeon of fear, well, maybe anxiety about what message(s) my body might send me."

"That is not unusual. The naturopathic view suggests everything we think, do, eat, breathe, feel and experience goes into the mix of our health. It can be unsettling to begin viewing your health this way."

"I abide by this view, I really do, even as I watch myself consume too much caffeine or salty/crunchy things." My attempt at humor felt flat. So I got real and laid it on the line. "Those are my only two so-called vices left. I don't eat things with wheat, sugar, yeast, cheese or meat and mostly haven't for nineteen years since 1991 when I was diagnosed with systemic Candida." I heard her pen scratching a quick note and imagined she took notes in a giant almanac type journal with a quill pen.

"Also, I have taken several Relationship Systems Coaching courses and believe we are always in relationship to everything and everyone around us. It makes perfect sense, but it's hard to embrace when life gets challenging and I get caught up in my emotions."

I knew she was going to ask me the same questions I ask others to "unfold" the messages held within my body. "Unfolding" is a fancy jargon word for getting under the hood of things to uncover the genesis or flashpoint of an emotion or circumstance in order to release or neutralize the energy around it. I knew I was about to develop a deeper awareness of, and relationship with, my body and the pain or emotion causing the imbalance. My secret hope was to discover some genesis or flashpoint so profound my whole world would change. Knowing that to be my Perfectionista mask's set-up for disappointment, I decided to be content with discovering what my body needed from me to heal.

"I think that's all I need to say right now," I said.

"Okay, let's begin. Where are you sitting?"

"My favorite spot on the sofa," I said.

Outside my living room window, I saw Sunday afternoon beach goers gathered in clumps around the public picnic tables and grills. If I opened my window, I knew I'd smell just-lit charcoal and the burn off from lighter fluid. Memories of family vacations flooded in. My parents rented a beach cabin for a week each summer close to the tiny town of Freeport, Texas. Our first night there, before the fishing began, we always roasted weenies on coat hangers and made s'mores on a portable charcoal grill.

"Good." Dr. S's voice interrupted my reveries, "Settle into that favorite spot and then focus your awareness on your breath."

The air flowed cool into my nose, and the space between us was silent save for my audible breathing. "Sit crossed-legged, yogi-style, with your spine straight and cross your legs so that your left ankle bone is on top of and touching your right ankle bone." This was the exact opposite of the way I naturally sit cross-legged and felt awkward. "Now, extend your arms straight out in front of you, shoulder-height. Next, cross your left arm over the right at the wrists, palms facing and touching each other."

"Okay, I'm with you," I said, following her direction.

"Now move your hands toward your chest, elbows pointing out to the sides, fingers pointing down. Continue the rotation of your hands, fingers pointing toward your chest and as you continue to rotate your hands, bring your elbows down. Your fingers should be pointing up, pinkie fingers resting on your heart center, elbows by your sides." I got lost in the instructions about halfway through the rotation and the game *Twister* came to mind. I asked her to start the arm part again and the second time through, I managed to land my pinkies in-between my breasts on my heart-center.

"This isn't very comfortable," I said. "My ankles are pretty bony and I feel some pressure on my wrists bent like this." A rush of mild anxiety rose up through my spine, lodging in the back of my neck. "Relax. Release. Relax," I silently prayed, not wanting the tension to build into a headache.

"I know it feels different at first. But this position will help open your body's meridians." We sat in silence a moment as I battled mentally with the mask I call Brainiac who rolled her eyes and snickered at "body's meridians." I took a deep breath and concentrated on the ankle alignment, inviting Brainiac to join the beach goers.

"Close your eyes and move your tongue to the roof of your mouth. This opens the circuit to your meridians and helps you to focus." I realized I naturally place my tongue just so while meditating. "I'm going to use the Latin words for inhale and exhale. I want you to follow the rhythm of the words with your breath, inhaling when I say "Inspiritus" and exhaling when I say "Exspiritus." I inhaled slowly to her rhythm and held my breath for the few seconds before she said, "Exspiritus." These ancient words made breathing feel special. My fore-head un-creased and relaxed as I inspirited and exspirited. Next, my eyes released a squint that had lodged there after hearing "baggie" and "surgery."

I don't know how long she led me, because at some point I surrendered to a sense of timelessness. I no longer felt my ankles touching or my wrists crossed and folded. I was only aware of my chest rising and falling with each breath.

Her smooth voice sounded both close and safely distant when she asked, "Where do you feel the most energy in your body?"

Though accustomed to asking my clients that very question, it was my turn to body-scan. "My heart," I said.

"What does it feel like there in your heart?"

"It's cold and dark," I whispered. A soft yet steady cry began, like a gentle spring rain that leaves behind new buds nourished. "I hate that it's cold and dark in here. I pride myself on having a warm heart, and offering love is my thing," I said, cringing as I heard the words coming out of my mouth. As the internal Perfectionista chastised me, Dr. S assured me she knew my heart was full of love and generosity.

"What else do you sense here?" she asked.

"It feels lonely here," I squeaked out in between the growing sobs.

"What do you see in your cold and dark and lonely heart?"

"A refrigerator! I see a damn refrigerator in my heart." I was struck with a case of church giggles, Dr. S joining me.

When our laughter subsided, she asked me to see myself opening the door of the refrigerator. She paused the perfect amount of time and then asked, "What do you see in there?"

"It looks just like the inside of *my* refrigerator, except there are what look like forgotten boxes of leftovers behind the milk carton and the stacks of almond butter and yogurt containers. Restaurant meal leftovers in Styrofoam clamshell boxes fill the shelves of my heart." I sniffed in the refrigerator expecting a rotting food smell. There was no smell.

"What do you know about these boxes," Dr. S asked.

"These boxes warehouse leftovers of grief, anger and sadness." Before I could even think the thought, the words tumbled out of

my mouth. It was exactly what I'd told Veronica the morning after my visit with Dr. K.

Dr. S and I sat in silence for a moment before she asked me to open one of the clamshell boxes and look inside. I picked the square one, perfectly sized for hamburgers I don't eat. I slowly opened the top, half expecting some coiled snake to jump out at me. Instead, the container held one bite of something unrecognizable. I put it down and quickly opened and looked in the others. Each contained only a few bite-size morsels.

"Holy crap! I've already done the bulk of the emotional work! There are just remnants to deal with!"

Dr. S celebrated all the prior work I'd done around grief, anger and sadness, acknowledging the lightness in my voice. She then asked me to choose one box to work with. I chose the small square hamburger-less hamburger box.

"Open it again," she directed. "Really look at it. What do you see?"

I reopened the small square box and looked at the remnant bite. "Sadness."

"What does this sadness look like?" she asked.

"It is covered in black mold, sprouting a hairy avocado green mold, which has bright yellow and reddish spots, with more black mold sprouting on top of the red and yellow spots."

It reminded me of all the colors of mold growing on the walls and furniture of my brother's New Orleans home four weeks after Hurricane Katrina breached the levees. When the waters receded, they left dark lines at ten, eight and four feet on the inside and outside walls of the house, and a kaleidoscope of textured mold colors.

"How does it feel to view your sadness with mold growing on it?" Dr. S asked.

I braced myself for an avalanche of tears that didn't come. "It feels pretty neutral."

I didn't know what to do with the neutrality. Hot, cold, wild, passionate, devastated I get. Neutral was just plain puzzling.

"Feel into neutral," she directed.

"It feels like the fulcrum of a see-saw—not up and not down."

"Let's breathe here at the fulcrum for a moment," she said. We inspirited and exspirited together. "What do you notice now?"

"Well, neutral seems okay. Neutral isn't actually average or boring, which I always thought it was. I can go any direction from neutral." There it was, I'd just admitted my Overachiever mask's judgment that neutral equals boring.

"Anything else?"

"No. I want to know about the other boxes."

I opened the rectangular clamshell boxes one by one. Dr. S guided me into each one to experience their small moldy bites of grief and anger.

"What's here for you as you view these leftover emotions?"

"I'm shocked. How can these have no power over me?" Why wasn't I a sobbing mess? A chopstick magically appeared, and I poked at a moldy bite in the grief box. I poked harder and harder, thinking that would make me feel something. It didn't, and I wondered aloud if I'd become comfortably numb.

"What do you think?" Dr. S asked.

"I think I've been afraid to let go of my grief, sadness and anger. They are a little like battle scars, or badges of honor, reminding me of what I've been through. And can I just say how shitty that is to say?"

Thank God she didn't elaborate on how we all do that, or worse, offer some cliché about how we let go when we are ready to let go. In fact, she said nothing for a few moments, letting me feel into it all. Not only had I been prideful in wearing these damn scars, I'd been lazy about cleaning out my refrigerator. I felt a grand spring-cleaning on my physical body horizon.

"What do you want to do with these boxes of moldy, emotional leftovers?" Dr. S asked.

"Chuck 'em into the garbage like I do with leftovers on trash day." I already had the Hefty bag in my hand, but she slowed me down.

"What do you want to say to the leftover sadness?"

I held the small square box in my right hand and the open black Hefty bag in my left hand. It didn't feel possible that this small box could feel so heavy. "I'm done with the crying and feeling full of regret. I can't change the past and hanging onto you is the false hope that I can change it." Then I whispered, "I want to be free," and gently placed the box in the bag. Like a Harry Potter magic trick, the small square box filled up about half of the Hefty bag.

"What do you want to say to the leftover of grief?"

I picked up the deep rectangle box of grief. I stared at it trying to remember a time I wasn't actively grieving something or someone in the past ten years. I held the box eye level, peering into it like it was a snow globe. I saw myself sitting on the tile floor just inside the front door the night of October 30, 2005, sobbing as I sang made up lyrics to the tune of Amazing Grace to honor Chaub, the most fantastic golden retriever ever to live, who Rich and I had held as he took his last breaths early that morning. Chaub was our first fur-baby, and we were still reeling from Siena's (our second fur-baby) sudden death just five months earlier. Even though I was sobbing with all these thoughts and memories of losing Chaub, I can't recall his name without smiling.

Dr. S acknowledged my tears and said, "Just be with it, Cat. Just be."

That wave of grief rose up and felt like heartburn in my chest and I could taste the acid rising up from my stomach. I wanted to spit it out, but before I could it disappeared into the ether.

I saw my father lying in the hospital bed, smiling his half smile and it felt like my heart was torn in two all over again. I saw Scott and me, planning our life together before his esophagus ruptured and the rage of unfairness rose up inside me.

I refocused onto the leftovers and saw the words "and they lived happily ever after" inscribed on the bite splashed with the most colors of mold. Like a slap across the face, it hit me: death of the "happily ever after" dream with Rich was so hard to swallow and had become such a lingering grief because there was no body to bury or ashes to keep in an urn on the mantle. The grief for our baby, the pregnancy I chose to end, showed up and swirled around in the mold. I expected to experience the stomach bile sensation again. Instead, my chest felt squeezed, and I couldn't breathe for a moment.

I kept looking in the box and saw my gaunt, dark-circles-under-the-eyes self, staring at the empty side of the closet after Rich moved out. I saw that self move from the closet to curl up on the floor in a fetal position, next to his side of the bed, sobbing.

I gasped and began inspiriting and exspiriting with fervor, imagining the "body" of happily ever after coming out of my exhales like smoke tendrils. After the smoke was out of me and filled the clamshell box of leftovers, I said softly, "Goodbye grief. You may feel like an old familiar friend, but it is time to end this codependent shit." As I spoke those words aloud, I placed the grief box very gingerly in the Hefty bag, not wanting it to spring open from a casual toss.

"Cat, you are brave to be examining so deeply and releasing these leftovers. Do you want to continue or stop for now?"

"I'm ahead of you - I've already got the anger box in my hand."

"What does it feel like in your hand?" Dr. S asked.

"It doesn't have any weight. Maybe because the anger is all about what's in the other two boxes?" I started laughing and said, "I swear I can hear the Don Henley lyric right now about anger eating you up inside." I paused. Dr. S and I sat in silence.

"I'm done being eaten from the inside by my own anger," I said quietly without any charge. In fact, the kindness in my voice surprised me—I sounded like I was speaking to someone I loved who was suffering. Before Dr. S could instruct me to, I placed the third clamshell box in the Hefty bag and tied the corner flaps into knots.

Dr. S asked me to take a deep breath. When I inhaled, my lungs expanded wide and the rib just below my right shoulder blade didn't catch or poke or do whatever it does when it is out of alignment. I took another breath becoming aware of my body and realized my ankles felt like they were on fire and my hands were numb. I told Dr. S I had to move my body and she did her best to hurry the re-entry along, systematically. But I un-pretzeled my body, rotated my wrists to get some energy flowing into my hands as soon as I spoke, and pretended to follow her directions. I wondered, how many of my clients do the same thing when they are ready to be in the here and now after one of my guided meditations or healing sessions?

I glanced at the timer on my phone and yelped, "Yikes! I can't believe we've been on the phone for two hours! It doesn't seem like it at all, and at the same time, it feels like longer."

"How are you feeling right now?" Dr. S asked.

I gave myself a moment to check in. "I feel spent and energized at the same time, the way I imagine a marathon runner must feel crossing the finish line."

"I suggest you take very good care of yourself tonight. You did deep work today and your body will need rest and nurturing. Journaling can be a good way to continue processing."

I assured her I knew all the "right" things to do after a healing session. Drink plenty of water, no imbibing; eat a light meal, journal and take a warm Epsom salts bath.

"Cat, let's talk about what else you can be doing to physically support your body. I'm going to send you a recipe for alkalinizing green soup. Most of us eating a typical Western-style diet are too acidic and that creates an environment for dis-ease to thrive in."

"I'm familiar with the acidic/alkalinizing thing," I said, remembering all the reading I'd done about how to live a Candida-free life.

"Keep using your Release essential oil. And the supplements you are taking look good. Along with the green soup recipe, I'm going to send you a list of a few other supplements I think will help you right now."

I did a body scan and said, "Dr. S, I feel different in my body right now, lighter and more spacious. Like I've lost ten pounds or something. Thank you, truly." Though I felt grateful to my core for the session, I did not feel compelled to go into profuse, over-the-top thanks. "Thank you, truly," felt just right.

After the call, I sat for ten minutes or so, a complete blank. I experienced a distinct lack of thoughts and an even more distinct lack of emotions. I felt the peace I feel after a deep and long meditation. Time wasn't relative and to-dos weren't lunging at me. My cell phone's ring brought me back to earth's distractions even though I didn't answer the call.

Instead, I got in a hot bath with Epsom salts and my "Release" essential oil. Head resting on the bath pillow, body submerged, one knee bent and above the warmth of the water, I thought about the process that Dr. S used with me and realized it was a version of what I've been doing for years with clients and myself. My mind wandered to the Hefty bag of clamshell boxes, then I pondered "happily ever after" and the expectations I had wrapped around that fairytale notion. Though I'd lived outside of so many of the traditions and norms I was raised on, I saw that I had not escaped their internalization.

CHAPTER 18

Throwing Spaghetti with Vaishali

I promised myself at the end of my Healing Chamber experience with my sister-goddesses that I would stay open to any and all healing opportunities that felt intuitively right. The day of my Disneyland adventure, I received an email blast from Morgana Rae, friend, magical goddess and master money coach. (She's really good at all that Web/Internet stuff and she probably doesn't know it, but she's my Internet heroine. She had the foresight and courage in 2002 to see what I couldn't see about using the Internet to support and be of service to people.) Anyway, her email invitation to attend a telecall instantly intrigued me. Morgana would be interviewing Vaishali, a woman who healed herself from terminal illness twice without Western medicine, prescription drugs or surgery.

I clicked on the link to watch an interview of Vaishali. Her bright Spirit leapt off my laptop screen, and I could feel a kindred-spirit glow as she spoke. The title of one of her books, *You Are What You Love,* and Morgana's bottom line description

"Think Deepak Chopra in a slinky purple dress," sealed the deal. I entered the call in my calendar.

The year 2005 was one of loss and grief for my family: Rich and I lost two of our beloved dogs to spleen ruptures; a promising financial deal blew up in our faces; my brother lost his home in Hurricane Katrina, becoming a "double evacuee" after he and my mom had to evacuate her home to escape the path of Hurricane Rita. All the while, Rich and I were doing our best to ignore that the divide over having children was growing. By the end of the year, we couldn't seem to agree on much except we loved each other. One night, after tossing a handful of spaghetti on the refrigerator to see if it was ready, I decided my life philosophy would be "throw spaghetti and see what sticks." Both the spaghetti and the philosophy stuck.

After the initial shock of Dr. K's words wore off, I picked up my spaghetti philosophy again in earnest. I was curious what new tool I might learn from Vaishali, or what old tool I'd be reminded to use and would stick. I was equally curious about what might not ring true to me and would slide off. My spiritual and holistic approach to life was not without its misfires and disappointments, or "gurus" offering the next greatest modality since sliced bread. One guru even asked to borrow money, even though he knew Rich and I barely had our heads above water. No longer the naïve seeker, I had learned to trust my bullshit meter.

I dialed in for the start of the call. Vaishali's voice was filled with my favorite things: optimism, enthusiasm and Spirit. She drew me in immediately and my bullshit detector did not go off. Morgana invited her to tell about how she became Vaishali. Vaishali is the birthplace of Buddha and a word from the ancient and mostly unpracticed 3000-year-old language, Sanskrit. A shaman, with whom she had studied in India, had given her the name. Born with a facial birth defect, Vaishali was taunted as a child and even had rocks thrown at her by schoolmates. She underwent several cosmetic surgeries, obviously successful, as I could see from her appearance on the video I watched.

Her parents divorced early in her life, and her alcoholic mom married another volatile alcoholic and Vaishali suffered their raging anger and abuse. As a young adult in abusive relationships, she received two death-sentence diagnoses—one from a mysterious infection that defied any treatment. Though I had not been hospitalized as Vaishali had, my experience of Candida had led me to discover a holistic approach, which eventually healed me. For Vaishali, sugar was kryptonite. And like me, Vaishali also suffered from a near-fatal car accident.

Vaishali shared she had lived on the short end of the financial stick (totally relatable to some of my years with Rich) and been cheated on in relationships (yep, me, too, though not by Rich). Her studies included Ayurveda and Oriental medicine, which I've always been curious about; the "laying on of hands;" shamanic teachings and disparate historical texts of philosophers and scientists. Yes, yes and yes—this is my kind of gal, I thought—someone that can come through many adversities and make it her life's work to learn how to help others. Her message of love was right in line with my life purpose, "Know the light of love is inside. Share it!"

Byron Katie's work came to mind when Vaishali shared that the thoughts and emotions around her life experiences kept her miserable and sick long after the event. Much as I could relate, I

167

was beginning to wonder if I was going to learn anything new. In my mid-twenties I'd discovered during my Candida healing that speaking my truth and feeling my emotions were part of "curing" a sore throat. Now I was certain the growth on my right ovary was connected to all those emotions in the leftover boxes I'd examined with Dr. S.

Then, all of a sudden, I felt a tingle up my spine as Vaishali said it took shifting her emotional responses and *thinking about the way things should be* that helped her heal her body, mind, emotions and Spirit and brought her back from those death sentences. When my body responds actively with a tingle, I know to keep listening. I also knew that my thoughts about fertility, life with Scott, and all the choices I didn't make with Rich, were trapping me in a loop of emotional turmoil.

I don't know how many other people were on that telecall, but all of a sudden I felt like Vaishali was speaking to me directly. The part of me in need of healing surrendered. And because everyone, other than the host and interviewee, was muted, I was safe to be audibly vulnerable and do the work.

The release begun in my healing circle, expanded upon with Dr. S, resumed as Vaishali led us through a healing session. I nodded in agreement when Vaishali said we become dependent on anger and grief as some sort of psychic food. "Yes! I thought they would make me stronger!" I said out loud. At the same time I was thinking it, she said, "All they do is make you miserable and leave you feeling over-full and ill, like after a big indulgent holiday dinner." And when, I wondered, reflecting back on all of my own over-indulgences, did it become "de rigueur" to overeat to the point of feeling ill at Thanksgiving and Christmas?

Vaishali asked me to lie on my back, so I did. She directed me to place my hands under my rib cage and angle my fingers just so toward my spine. She asserted that I should be able to feel my spine, so I pushed and tried to massage my way there. A series of staccato farts escaped as I pushed on my innards. She said no matter how much extra physical weight we have on our bones our innards should be so flexible we should be able to feel our spine. I kept pushing down with my fingers, trying to feel my spine. At once, I believed it was possible and simultaneously I thought, "Bullshit!" though I continued to mash around and fart.

For the second time in twenty-four hours I heard strains in my inner ear of Don Henley song lyrics: "Let go of all the anger, it'll eat you up inside." My stomach contorted as if to heave up some deeper chunk of leftover anger at God for letting daddy die in spite of my kidney. Another contortion heaved up a rock of anger at myself for singing the refrain from "Midnight Train to Georgia" for so many years, "I'd rather live with him in his world than without him in mine." Another stomach contortion heaved up a rock of anger at myself for not making the break from Rich when our relationship was on the table during our almost seven-year itch. Another rock of anger came loose called debt—the debt we ran up in my name because of his business' shift. My chest then tensed involuntarily as Vaishali went through the impact on the body of different habitual emotions. I realized I'd been in an involuntary "squeezed" state for some time. My old anger and grief were like junk food and every bit as crave-inducing it turns out. I was glad the conference line was muted because when Vaishali said it was time to have a giant emotional bowel movement, I laughed so hard I missed the next minute or so. I found myself wishing it were that simple to instantly and forever release emotional waste.

I missed what she said next, too, because I was in my own aha moment. *I have been seeking safety in my left-over anger and grief so I won't be hurt again."* As if that will work," I snorted to the footstool on my left. Still on my back, head rolling from side to side, I tried to deny that I might be the one perpetuating the hurt and harm—physical, emotional and mental.

"Forgiveness." I stopped the self-recrimination when I heard Vaishali say the word. "Forgiveness doesn't mean you let people off the hook! They did the bad, wrong, evil thing. It doesn't wipe the transgression away," she explained.

Forgiveness simply means you get to move beyond whatever the pain is and step into something new.

The therapist I saw after Daddy died introduced me to the notion of self-forgiveness. She opened the door for me. It took me a long time to walk into the space of it. Once I got the hang of it, though, I sought the possibilities self-forgiveness opened.

"Yes, new is what I want," I said aloud. "Yes, I want to forgive myself anew. Yes, I have the power of now. Yes, I can move beyond the hurt and pain I caused myself. Yes, I can move beyond the self-betrayal. Yes, I can move beyond the grief." I felt a softening in my stomach, the tension relaxing. I poked my fingers just under my rib cage again. My innards were definitely softer, but I still couldn't feel my spine.

"You are divine love and wisdom," Vaishali said. It reminded me of an affirmation I made up to focus on my life purpose: Love, light, peace. I don't remember if she said to repeat it out loud or I decided it would be good for me to repeat the phrase. Each time

I repeated, "I am divine love and wisdom," my breathing slowed and deepened, and my voice turned to a whisper. Though still lying on my back in the path of sunshine streaming through the sliding glass door, I had given up trying to feel my spine. I alternated whispering, "All Love, All The Time," and "I am Divine Love & Wisdom Now." Off in chant-land, I missed some of Vaishali's bridging thoughts and questions. I tuned back just in time to hear her particular twist on what I'd been practicing and sharing for years: "You are What You Love and You Love What You Give Your Attention To." The idea is that when we place our intention and attention on something, like a goal or outcome, the energy surrounding it grows. Though the message was not new, it felt like an affirmation of all that I was doing to heal.

Aloud, I spoke defensively, "I don't *love* feeling angry. I don't love feeling anxious. I don't love experiencing grief." Then my tough gal pride chimed in tersely, "I am also not afraid of feeling these emotions." And like cold water being thrown on my unconscious self, I stopped mid-thought. Yes, I can be with and handle my own emotional meltdowns. Yes, I can be with friends and clients in theirs. My wacky pride around being able to handle any emotional torment on my own, without help, had me stuck repeating patterns like a broken record. Then in one of those super-fast yet super-slow-motion experiences, I got the distinction: "being with" and "being stuck in" are two different things entirely. "Being with" feels full of big space, permission and gentleness. "Stuck in" feels closed, judgmental and full of sharp edges.

Don Henley's lyrics taunting me again, I stood up, trying to pace off my agitation. "I want to change, I want to *change*. Yes, I *want* to change."

"So let's change!" was the quick advice from JoyFullLight, my Future Self. "Let's ditch the broken record and change the music fast, honey." She conjured up the image of the red portable turntable in my childhood bedroom. I saw my arm reach out and lift the needle and move it to another section of the vinyl record that played smoothly. No scratches. No getting stuck. "Ahhhh," she said and was gone.

When I came out of my reverie, Vaishali was saying our thoughts are psychic food, affecting the wellbeing of the body. To heal from Candida, I had to change my diet and re-work my thoughts and practice self-forgiveness. During that time, I lived the mind-body connection. When I heard Vaishali say that I can tell my body what I want for it, especially through my visualizations, I made a giant checkmark on the inner screen of my mind and said, "Yep, I'm already doing that." But it felt important to be reminded that I can love my body back into balance.

I listened to the pitch to schedule a private session with Vaishali or attend her workshop that weekend. Mildly interested, I flipped open my calendar, but saw the days she was offering private sessions were already booked out in my schedule. And a whole weekend trying to reach my spine from under my rib cage didn't feel like the best use of my healing time. Throwing spaghetti isn't about re-arranging all the pots, pans and colanders in the cupboard; it is about showing up and seeing what sticks.

Vaishali's focus on positive affirmations, forgiveness, being in charge of my body, thoughts and emotions was like taking a yellow highlighter pen to my inner game playbook. The best part was, I could feel myself un-sticking from the pain I caused myself in the past. "Yesterday I threw out moldy leftovers. Today I wipe off the outside of the refrigerator and clean up the old spaghetti."

After the call was over my thoughts drifted to a Sunday afternoon in late April when I was seventeen. My brother's hand-me-down Camaro, nicknamed the Silver Bullet, had become stuck in the sand on a local Texas beach about an hour from my hometown. It was where we went to meet up with teenagers from other schools and listen to loud music blaring from any guy's oversized speakers in the back of his pick-up truck. Oh yeah, we also drank a lot of beer. Marian, one of my wild-child friends and I met up with some other wild-child friends for a day of fun in the sun. Marian and I stayed later than the rest. (I needed to sober up before the drive back to town.) It was almost 6:00 p.m. when I finally took the wheel, way past the hour I should have been headed home. Knowing I was going to be late, and imagining the parental lectures that would await me, I pressed the gas pedal to the floor, and went nowhere. The harder I pressed the gas pedal, the deeper the car sank in the sand, and the more sand flew in through the open windows, plastering the red interior. I became frantic when I realized I could no longer even open my car door.

A lean, shirtless, overly tan older guy walking along the water's edge drinking Lone Star beer from a long neck bottle heard me gun the engine the second time. He jogged over, waving his free hand in front of his face in the universal sign to cease whatever you are doing, immediately.

He leaned into my window a little breathless and said, "Darlin', the more yew spin dem tires, the harder it's gonna be for me to pull ya outta here! Unload yer trunk, remove the ice chest from your backseat and I'll be back wid my truck and git ya'll on yer way." Since I had managed to sink the car so low the doors wouldn't open my friend crawled out of the window and I handed her the ice chest.

You just have to love how gallant a good ole' boy Texan man can be. Most of them want to feel like they have accomplished something helpful, like jump starting your car, pulling you out of a ditch or changing your tire. This one pulled my Camaro out of the soft sand with his enormous, late 70's Chevy pick-up truck. For his trouble, I gave him the rest of the Lone Star beer from the ice chest.

I was *very* late in getting home. My mom was in the driveway before I even turned off the engine, my father not far behind. I had asked Marian to call them after I dropped her off to let them know I would be home shortly. I saw their looks of frustration give way to concern when I directed their gaze to the sand plastered on the inside of the car. Rather than being punished, I wound up with a mini-lecture and sympathy—maybe because they could see my remorse. I had also called them from the first roadside pay phone after getting unstuck.

I wondered, how often I'd gotten unstuck because of kindly strangers and helpful loved ones? I have several file folders full of "love letters" from clients thanking me for getting them unstuck. Help. Yes, asking for help is a good thing. So is receiving it.

After mashing my innards around with Vaishali, I decided to stretch out the rest of me with some yoga and turned on my favorite Enya CD.

CHAPTER 19

Conjuring Up Ghosts
in Child's Pose

I inhaled slowly, consciously expanding my ribs, held my breath for a moment and exhaled what felt like more than air. I was in my next to final yoga posture, Child's Pose, and suddenly, there he was: Daddy.

He had not appeared spontaneously in quite some time. That's the thing about the dead . . . you never know when their Spirit will show up. This time he wore his circa 1977 khaki green fishing jumpsuit. He looked as relaxed as he always did on his bright orange boat, the *Vagabond II*. The only things missing were a fishing rod in one hand and a can of Schlitz beer in his other.

I resisted the urge to move and stayed folded like an accordion. The tops of my feet and shins rested on the towel, my knees bent so that the backs of my thighs lay against my calves and my buttocks touched my heels. My chest lay comfortably on the top of my thighs, arms alongside my folded legs, forehead on the towel. I took another deep breath and noticed the towel was slightly damp from sweat and rough on my forehead. I kept my eyes closed, entranced by the presence and image of my father.

Daddy smiled at me, his deep-set blue eyes sending a wave of love and warmth through me. My God I've missed his ready smile and the enjoyment of life in his eyes. I smiled back my twenty-one years of missing him. Moments, minutes, hours and years collapsed into the "power of now" Eckhart Tolle talks about.

"You are fine," Daddy told me, his words slow and deliberate. A belt of tightness around my chest loosened. I sensed he was telling me he had taken care of the growth, and it wasn't anything to worry about. I breathed deeply again, trusting him.

I heard his voice both inside my head and with my ears. I felt him sitting in the room with me, on my sofa and resisted the yearning to lift my head and open my eyes. I remained curled in Child's Pose.

He continued, "Remember, we've been down this road before." I remembered. I spent that Thanksgiving weekend doubled over in pain, my lower right side aching from the cyst that ruptured a few weeks later when I lifted a tray of dirty dishes working for a caterer. We had scheduled the surgery for when I returned home for Christmas vacation.

Lying there in Child's Pose, a throbbing sensation began around my right ovary. Not a painful or scary throbbing, but a good throbbing, like the way muscles respond after a strenuous workout. I saw an image of my ovary glowing like a rose quartz crystal.

"I am always here for you," Daddy said softly and reassuringly. I felt tears as my body melted further into Child's Pose. The tears pooled and dripped from the top of my nose where it joins my forehead, running across my third eye on their way to my hairline, merging with sweat.

My dear friend Connie's father died when she was nineteen. We have said many times over the years how we long for one more conversation with our fathers. And here it was for me. But I didn't have to ask the questions I've longed to ask him. He already knew them, and it was pretty much a one-way conversation. When the flicker of a new thought or question began to form inside of me, he answered before my words could fully form the sentence in my brain.

Daddy was a typical man of his generation, dedicated to and defined by his role as provider for his family. He didn't change many diapers or clean the house, but he grilled a mean steak, and showed up for his family. As I lay curled on the floor, I was transported back to my fifth-grade softball season, my father in the bleachers bellowing during the second inning, "In the name of humanity, call the game, Ump." My last-place team was already losing by double digits. In each venue, as I watched my memories run by like movie clips, I was pulled inside my father's point of view. I watched with him from the audience my junior high play performances of title roles like *Pegora the Witch* and *Heavens to Betsy*. Then, we moved to my high school's football stadium where I saw myself as drum major leading the all-girl drum and bugle corps onto the field at halftime. In those glimpses, I experienced the enormity of his love for and pride in me. Though generous with gifts and acts of service to show his love, he had not been great at expressing his feelings verbally. Neither had I, except when our Aries horns were locked in battle over the lack of material in my bikinis, questionable boyfriends and the usual teenage angst stuff. Twenty years of "why" and "why not" questions evaporated in those precious seconds sitting in his perspective.

Once returned from his perspective to my living room, still curled into child's pose, I heard his voice, not inside me but out loud.

"The lesson here is to receive love." His voice held that infrequent demanding note, like when he would tell me to do something as a kid, "Cat, rake the front yard this afternoon after school."

"But I've learned to ask for help," I protested, thinking about my healing circle. Yes, he agreed that I'd learned to ask for help.

"And I do know I'm loved," I said.

"Yes, you know," he said tapping the right side of his head with his index finger. He leaned forward in that way of his that commanded attention, his eyes focused and his demeanor serious rather than his more natural teasing tone. My mind became like his etch-a-sketch where he wrote as he spoke: "And now it is time to take the next step and receive love. *Let it in. Experience it.*"

I exhaled, trying to grasp the magnitude of what he was saying.

Then he dropped the bombshell on me. "Cat, this was my lesson, too. It took the ultimate act of receiving your kidney for me to learn to *receive* love." He said he had gotten the lesson, but the years of his own grief (his father died when Daddy was twenty), professional stress and not knowing how to receive love had taken such a toll on his body, he couldn't continue to live on this plane. Tears engulfed me. I needed to blow my nose but just let the towel absorb the mucous and tears. I didn't dare leave the moment.

The scar from my kidney donation wraps around the right side of my waist, and in that moment it tingled with the heat of release. Guilt, grief, shame, and anger let go of me as I had let

178

go of them around Rich a few days earlier during my session with Dr. S.

Relaxing back again as if he were on his fishing boat, Daddy continued. He said his ego had gotten the better of him, and that I was not to let mine stop me from truly receiving love. "You don't need to keep making the same mistakes I did, Cat. Cure your ego now." I wanted to argue like I argued almost every edict with him, but this one rang true.

"Cat, I love you dearly." He paused, emotion welling up in him. "I always have. I always will." With each of those tenderly spoken words, I felt an unwinding. It began in my mind, moved to my heart, then dropped to my stomach and finally unbound a piece of my soul. His love of me nestled between my heart and solar plexus. As if he knew what had just happened, he smiled and said again, "I am *always* here for you."

I felt a physical-sensation of warmth on my mid-back, the size and shape of his earthly hand. The warmth radiated through me like sunshine, and felt primal, fierce, protective and gentle all at once. His hand lingered on my back for a few more moments and then he was gone.

I stayed in Child's Pose, waves of energy coursing through me. His words had felt warm and buttery. I ran the conversation over in my head, letting it settle into me. I experienced what some in the healing arts call the electric shock—meaning, I jerked a few times as if struck by electricity, when replaying his words, "Cat, this was my lesson too."

The more I reflected on the conversation, the more I experienced those electric shocks. I took a deep inhale, lifting and arching my chest and settling back down into a deeper stretch of my spine, repeating the pattern three more times. With each inhale I became more confident in knowing I could let in love. With each exhale I released pieces of panic and fear. And control. My tears flowed slow and gentle. The room was completely dark when I slowly uncurled my spine, sitting for a moment longer with my legs folded beneath me before lying flat on my back. I'd been in Child's Pose from the beginning of sunset to complete darkness and should have felt much more joint stress in my knees than I did. There was no doubt in my being about what had just transpired. I knew I was not going to need surgery the following week.

More important was the knowing I no longer needed to carry the remnants of guilt about not saving my daddy's life. I touched the scar on my waist and what turned out to be a rather prophetic dream in February 1989, three months before the kidney transplant, rose up in me. That week, my father had been hospitalized due to dialysis complications and blood pressure spikes and dips. We were all worried the transplant would have to be postponed. Secretly, I was worried we may have waited too long. My Daddy's mom, my Mam-Maw, stood in a field of pink flowers dressed in her favorite pink knit Chanel-like suit and said in her unhurried drawl, "It doesn't matter what you do, Darlin." I guess it hadn't. And then again . . . "It took the ultimate act of receiving your kidney for me to learn to *receive* love," . . . perhaps it really had.

CHAPTER 20

Galveston ...
Oh Galveston ...

A family friend's two-bedroom condo in Galveston, close to the hospital where my father fought for his life, was my family's home base and had been since the week before the transplant in May 1989. These family friends were bonded to my parents via their med school experiences, as well as riding out Hurricane Carla together in 1961. They said the timing was perfect for us to arrive in mid-May as their daughter had just finished her schooling and would be moved out by then.

At 2:39 a.m. central time in late September of 1989, while snuggled in the bed of the small second bedroom of that condo, a bright light in the far corner ceiling awakened me. It was silvery like the moon or a giant theatrical spotlight, bathing me in its light.

Attempting to make rational sense of it, I ran through possibilities. It can't be lightening, I thought since I heard no thunder, and the light remained steady and bright. My heart began to race with confusion and a hint of fear. I'd had visits from Mam-Maw before, my father's mother, but always in my dreams and she never woke me with a bright light.

I attempted to roll from my back onto my left side only to discover my body felt leaden . . . though strangely I also couldn't really feel my body. I also couldn't stop looking at the bright light, still hovering in the corner. It was beautiful. It was magnetizing. "Am I dreaming?" I wondered. My whole body felt the way my foot feels when I sit on it for a while—that "asleep" feeling of numbness. I tried to move again, hoping to experience the prickly feeling as blood flow returns. Nothing.

At that point, the light grew brighter and filled the entire room as if the sun itself was in there. It felt like I was having my own personal *Close Encounters of the Third Kind* only I wasn't in a movie. The voice in my head said, "Run," but when I tried to sit up, an anvil like pressure pressed down on my chest, pinning me to the bed and pushing what felt like the last of the air out of my lungs. "What is happening to me?" my mind shrieked. Panic set in, and my mind raced through possibilities.

"Am I having a heart attack? A stroke like daddy?" Suddenly the neurologist's words to me after many tests about my headaches roared in, "Like many migraine sufferers, your veins are under-sized." I'd read later in his report that those smaller veins could contribute to an aneurism.

In trying to move one body part at a time I discovered the only thing I *could* move was my head, so I turned my head to look at the clock and saw the digits move from 2:39 to 2:40.

I opened my mouth to yell, "HELP," to my mother in the other bedroom but only a dry, silent scream came out. I began to cry, feeling like my nightmares of not being able to scream when being attacked were happening in real life. But what was attacking me? The light was beautiful, felt warm and seemed filled with love. Feeling weak and lightheaded, I stopped fighting, hoping if I lay there motionless, the weight of the anvil pushing me into the bed would lessen. I wondered how long it would take for unconsciousness to set in as I gulped for air like a fish out of water.

A sudden fury overtaking me, my mind screamed, "This is *not* how it ends."

At the exact same moment my mind screamed, the bright light vanished, like a candle snuffed out, and the anvil lifted. I sat up as though my torso were on a spring and gasped for air like I'd just sprinted for a mile, sweating and cold at the same time. Part of me was screaming, "What the hell just happened?" yet my brain seemed only able to focus on my body, so I stood up to be sure my legs still worked.

I went to the door of my mom's bedroom and heard her snoring. I continued to the bathroom to splash water on my face. My throat parched from dry screams, I guzzled a glass of water and got back in bed. Though I was wrung out I began processing the experience.

What is the message I wondered? Much of my guidance comes from dreams. I had the repetitive childhood dream of dying in a fire, no one able to get to me to save me (later in a quasi past-life regression I discovered being burned at the stake, which I had sensed even as a child). And then there's the time I dreamed about being a passenger in a car wreck with a boy I was dating and then was in a car wreck with a train the next day with the boy I was dating. I'm also prone to getting feelings when something bad has happened to a loved one—like when I was walking across campus my junior year of college. I suddenly knew I needed to return to my dorm room and call home. By the time I got back to my room and called, my body was shaking. I could feel that something horrible had happened. When my mom answered the phone, I could tell she was crying. "What's wrong?" I asked. She told me that Hart, my beloved cousin, one year younger than me, had been murdered.

Then there was the time I was about to go sailing for the afternoon on my date's boat and that wave of "something's wrong" washed over me. I jumped off the boat and ran to the dock's pay phone. My brother said he'd just bought a plane ticket for me to Port Arthur after Daddy collapsed and was admitted to ICU. But this experience of a bright light shining in the corner of the room, with an anvil weight on my chest was very different. I was involved in the experience somehow, like in my nightly dreams. But it wasn't a dream, I thought, drifting into a deep sleep. I didn't move again until my mom gently tapped my shoulder to wake me.

Over coffee, sitting at the glass-top dinette table I started to share my bizarre nighttime experience with my mother.

"Are you sure you weren't just dreaming Cat? You have quite the imagination . . ."

"Oh no, it was not a dream," I said vehemently. "It was real. I could not move, could not scream for you and could not breathe."

I saw her wanting to believe me between deep drags on her Virginia Slims Ultra Light.

"Mom, it was like what people say who died but came back. The light was really bright and inviting. But that's not what was happening because I didn't feel that freedom those people also talk about—I was pinned to the bed and unable to breathe." I could see her doubt and confusion, mirroring my own doubt and confusion.

Both of us jumped when the phone rang. She answered and after a very brief conversation with Dr. Jones, Daddy's doctor, she said, "We need to get ourselves over to the hospital."

Walking casually into Surgical ICU had become our daily routine. Most patients only stay a few days to recuperate from serious surgery. My father's med school friends and colleagues who worked at John Sealy Hospital moved mountains for him to stay in that ICU, knowing he needed stepped up care. (That would never be allowed in today's system.) I stood outside his tiny room watching a nurse futzing about with IVs and beeping monitors. His chart lay open on the rolling cart just outside the door where I was. I eyeballed it, wondering if I'd be able to read any of the writing on it today.

I froze and felt the same pressure on my chest when my eyes found 2:39 a.m. on the page. I backed away, afraid to keep reading. I looked at my father and confirmed with my own eyes he was alive and awake.

"What happened at 2:39 a.m.," I asked the nurse when she came out of my father's room, trying to sound casual.

She looked at me over the top of her reading glasses, deciding whether she was going to tell me or not. Daddy's doctors were the ones who gave us the updates.

I repeated, "What happened at 2:39 a.m. last night?" in a very deep voice that didn't sound like mine.

She sighed and said quietly, "Your father's heart stopped." I felt mine stop with her words, my eyes staring at her. "But we got it restarted very quickly, though, and he is holding his own right now," she said in a voice to perk me up.

I turned my head from her to him. She said, "Go ahead in— I'm through with my morning rounds. Let me know if y'all need anything." In spite and probably because of my daddy's hellish medical situation, ninety percent of his nurses were amazingly supportive, letting us ignore visiting hour mandates. They trusted that as a surgeon's family, we weren't going to get in the way of their work.

I went into Daddy's room and pushed the mauve pink chair close to the bed and held his hand. He rolled his head toward me and gave as much of a smile as he could. Oh, he didn't hold back on the smile, it's just that only half of his face moved since the stroke. I knew better than to cry in front of him and whispered, "Thanks for the visit last night, Daddy."

Mom came in just then, having stopped to confer with the doctor. I had decided a few weeks prior I couldn't be in on the daily conversations about every little up and down in my father's condition. Daddy beamed his half smile at her, and she got busy telling him all the news of the morning—who had pitched the night before for the Houston Astros, what the score was, who she had spoken with on the phone, and that she was glad to see him smiling this morning.

I felt my tears about to explode out of me so I made up the excuse of needing to visit the Ladies' room and left, knowing my mom was just ramping up and would be chatting for a while.

I needed to process what was happening, so I went down to the hospital chapel and pulled out a book of psalms. I wanted to tear it apart. "Lies, lies and more lies," my mind raged, finding no comfort. Daddy needed to live, dammit. He needed to recover from the stroke, come home and LIVE. That's why we did the kidney transplant—so he could LIVE—not lie there, paralyzed, or struggle with his heart stopping.

"Grandmommy says there is comfort here if I let there be. OK —let it in, Cat, let it in." I sank onto the kneeling bench, sobbing. I was born from daddy's seed in this very hospital. I was nurtured and loved by him. And now, my right kidney was inside his body. Did he experience what I experienced last night? Did he see a staggeringly bright light in one of the upper corners of his room? Did he feel like an anvil was on his chest? I cried harder at the thought of Daddy being scared like I was, wondering if it was the end for him. What kind of chaos had gone on in his room? No doubt the attending nurses turned on the obnoxiously bright overhead light—the beeping monitors must have been a loud and insistent cacophony. Oh, God—did anyone shout, "Code blue" or were the electric paddles used to shock his heart? Was it God or Daddy's light that was in my room? I sat with the awe-filled question, the thought of it being either or both, somehow calming. I remained on my knees, my tears running quietly, softly. Will I forever feel what is happening with Daddy? Does he feel me? Is this what other transplant donors and recipients meant when they said, "forever connected" in all the pamphlets I'd read pre-op?

A family came in to pray together. I could see they were in as much torment as I and that they needed to howl and pray out loud together, in private, so I stood up to leave.

"Oh, you don't need to go," the crying woman said.

"Yes, I do. I need to get back to my loved one." They nodded in understanding.

CHAPTER 21

The Body, The Body, The Body

"How did I get here?" I asked myself almost daily after hearing I needed surgery. Just like during the Candida turn-around, I knew uncovering the "how" was key to my healing going forward. Staying conscious about what I know and have learned are key tools in my confronting any challenge, and especially a health one.

As if to deny the legitimacy of what I saw on the ultrasound machine that morning in early March, I kept telling myself I wasn't in pain. And it was true. Sort of, though I had experienced the occasional twinge of discomfort in my lower right side for a few months. But not real pain.

I chalked up the twinges to ovulation. I had felt my right ovary ovulate for years, so I wasn't concerned about the twinge the Thursday evening two months earlier. During a yoga session at home I couldn't hold the T-pose on my right leg. The posture is really fun to move into. On a deep inhale, you raise your arms above your head, and step one foot forward and on the exhale, slowly hinge forward at the hips forming a "flat back" while lifting the opposite leg behind you, making a T with your body. Another name for this pose is Warrior III. Each muscle in the supporting leg and hip is fully engaged; your abs must be squeezed tight at the same time the gluteus and hamstring muscles of the leg lifted behind you are held strong. With my arms straight out in front of me, I feel a little like a superhero flying through space! This pose requires overall body concentration and mental focus in order to stay steady and still for eight slow inhale-exhale breathing cycles. To help me hold the pose, I pick a spot on the floor to focus on, like dancers pick a spot when they spin and whirl.

"For crying out loud in church," I said, exasperated as I tried for the third time that January night to sustain my T-pose. With each attempt, I held the pose for fewer breaths. Instead of getting curious about what was happening, I got mad at my body. Through gritted teeth, I completed the last four poses of my yoga set.

That should have been my first clue that the dominating, masculine energy mask, Chief Operating Officer of Control, had taken over to make me feel safe and more in charge.

Uncurling from the last pose of my yoga routine, the nasty, self-recriminating accusations from my Perfectionista mask began, "You're lazy, un-toned, out of shape and a fat sloth." Feeling betrayed by my body's inability to hold the T-pose, I couldn't slough off the slurs, even though my heart and bathroom scale knew them to be untrue. Like a runner who lights a cigarette after a run, I filled a small glass bowl with something salty and crunchy, as if to spite the Perfectionista.

I knew of three options that could pull me out of the yawning hell spiral of the powerful mask adorning me. 1. Soak in a bath of Epsom salts. 2. Put on the Sanskrit chant CD. 3. Journal.

Armed with the defiant bowl of my favorite organic blue corn tortilla chips, I opened my journal, a lifetime friend who tells it like it is. I stared at the blank page for a few moments working up the courage to face the truth and wrote: "I know not being able to hold the T-pose on my right leg indicates I'm out of balance. What's up?"

I admit, some of my journal writes are really b-o-r-i-n-g and more about my to-dos and the ways I'm managing them (or not). But that January night, it was as if I was not the one moving my pen across the page in answer to "What's up?" I tried to ignore phrases like "no baby" and "frustrated by" as I wrote.

Then, onto the page flew the words, " . . . like an episode of *Twilight Zone*." I stopped writing, closed my eyes and slumped back on the couch, recalling my favorite episode of this 1960's TV show, "The After Hours." When a lone woman shopper, a former mannequin, arrives on the non-existent top floor of a department store, the dapperly dressed mannequins come to life, as if ordered up by the woman. I sat up straight, eyes flying open.

"Holy crap! I'm trying to move people around like mannequins in a department store window." Okay, not people. Me. And Scott. I was trying to construct my vision of happy couple, happy home, with happy baby. Classic Chief Operating Officer of Control. Crunch, crunch, munch go the blue corn chips.

I paused my TV daydream and read what I'd just written. My trusted, truth-telling buddy the journal revealed I'd indeed entered a Twilight Zone-like battle of control where there could not possibly be a winner. I'd succumbed to my inner child's need to control the flow of events in life, and conversations with Scott. I wrote about how unhappy it made both of us I when I couldn't control my sharp inhale of breath at his quick lane changes or my shrieks to "Stop tailgating!" His response? To drive faster while I silently vowed to never let him drive again. I wrote about how pointless it felt to argue, splitting hairs over a political issue when we share the same philosophies. I wrote about and felt profound remorse about the hurt puppy-dog look on his face after I quipped, "You do know that dark socks worn with tan suede shoes offends the female species?"

The aftermath of each hellish attempt to control him and our relationship only spiraled me further into imbalance. I was too scared to ask him, "Why haven't you asked me to marry you? Why aren't you moving heaven and earth to get me pregnant?" I didn't want to hear his accountant-like nonsense about proper planning, timing, and finances. I also didn't want to see the obvious—he was still wiped out from the dramatic change in his body after the esophageal rupture. He was still trying to rebuild *his* stamina, resources and work life. So I questioned his driving skills. I argued, "Our country is running out of time to (fill in the blank)," instead of saying, "*We* are running out of time." And the most terrifying questions I tried to keep even from myself: Am I in the same relationship with a different man? Am I doomed to take care of him instead of being taken care of? Does he still really want to marry and have a family with me, like he says he does, or is he fooling himself, fooling me, and trying not to disappoint either of us?

My body, just like the tarot cards or runes, speaks truth to me when I connect to it. And just like the cards, you have to actually draw a card to receive the guidance. But when I've gone away from what I know, if I'm not asking and listening for the wisdom, I don't hear anything. "Oh, Cat, the body, the body, the body . . . it just doesn't lie," I said aloud, closing my journal and popping the last of the blue corn chips into my mouth, savoring the salt and the sound of the crunch.

"Hey, wait a minute," I thought, bouncing out of my own *Twilight Zone* marathon. "My ovary is twinging! That means I'm ovulating! Of course, that's why I can't hold the pose on that side!" I sent Scott a text saying, "I can't wait to see you this weekend!!! ;D ;D" to which he immediately responded, "Good! Me, too! :)" It was as if the reply from Scott shut down all my uneasiness, though nothing had actually changed.

After that night in January, I decided to focus my Chief Operating Officer of Control's need to control on the one thing I *could* exercise control over—my body. I got busy in my head to *solve* the imbalance problem. I didn't consult the Tarot cards or ask my body what it needed. I decided I knew. No wonder I couldn't hear its cries. I'd become a selective listener to my body's messages, as I had been when my father lay dying in ICU and I began to get bladder infections.

I upped my running schedule, advanced from "ramp it up" to "burn it up" on the "Slim in 6" exercise DVD, and ordered another DVD, Mari Windsor's "Pilates for the Stars," that promised a strong and toned body. Running longer distances required more visits to the chiropractor. "Burn it Up" did give me tight buns. The Pilates DVD by Windsor was a bust because I didn't have a door with enough space in front of it to attach the long cords and actually do the exercises. However, strengthening my gluteus muscles with extra running and all those "Burn it Up" squats, lunges and kicks tricked me into thinking

I was OK. Because in February, I wobbled less in the T-pose and assumed ovulation had switched to the left ovary.

A few short weeks after congratulating myself on conquering my wobble, I stopped running and lunging. "First, we'll baggie your ovary . . ."

Dr. K's words changed everything. I stopped pushing my body. I stopped pushing, period. Her words were the call to come out of my cave, to stop pretending. I could no longer lead my life with my masculine and controlling energy. It was time to re-step onto the path of my *heroine's* journey.

The heroine's journey is different than the hero's journey. It's the opposite of going it alone and battling monsters. It's about reclaiming the feminine way and the deep wisdom found within our bodies. I could not believe how far I'd strayed from my Modern Goddess priestess self. I felt adrift from the very thing I'd crafted my adult spiritual life around, the feminine side of divinity. The thing I've provided for hundreds of women since the first workshop I led in 1994. My priestess was still alive and well for everyone else but felt gagged and tied up in the corner when it came to me. Which is exactly where she'd been during the six-month siege in the ICU when my father was dying; exactly where she'd been during the last years with Rich; exactly where she was now as I did everything I could to ensure my body would stay fertile. And exactly where I was with Scott.

The irony is getting pregnant is something only a woman can do. I saw the absurdity in me approaching it from masculine energy. When I am centered in my feminine energy, I dance in the flow with the Universe. When I am centered in my masculine energy, I tend to lock my Aries horns with life.

How many times have I told Modern Goddess workshop participants and clients, that tapping into our feminine energy is the best way to receive what we desire?

After hearing "surgery" from Dr. K, I sorted all my exercise DVD's into piles—feminine flow of easy and gentle, the middle ground of moderate intensity, and masculine get it done extreme. I put the "Burn it Up" extreme stuff in the back of the drawer for another day. Yoga became slow and gentle, postures held for only four breaths. I "took walks" in my living room to a Leslie Sansone DVD my mom sent me for busy days when I didn't have time for a walk on the beach. (I wondered—is it sad or cool to use my mother's cast-off walking DVD? Cool, I decided.)

At each day's "move my body" time, I stood in my living room, palms pressed to my heart chakra, and asked my body what kind of movement it wanted to do. Usually, I would hear, "Slow and gentle yoga" or "Easy walk" or "Ramp it Up." When I didn't hear anything, I'd get more specific and ask, "Dear body, do you want to do yoga today?" I'd wait for my body's applied kinesiology response. My body shifts forward for yes, or backward for no. The form of exercise that got the yes from my body is what I did. When there was no yes, I didn't do any exercise.

I'd always thought that all the vigorous exercise, healthy eating, and meditating I did would prevent any major body issues from arising again. Perhaps the greatest gift of the ovarian growth was that I re-committed to listening to, partnering with, and honoring what my body wanted in new, and even deeper ways than I did before. Listening to my body, I realized it didn't approve of my habit of releasing emotions through strenuous physical exercise. It wanted me to choose more wisely, and not with my controlling brain. It wanted my respect. It wanted me to ask and pay attention to the answers. It wanted me to love it. It wanted me to reclaim my feminine side for *myself*.

When the body is hurting, we have choices: ignore it and hope it goes away, or address the pain we feel. Alternating between ignoring and controlling this body of mine had not made the twinge in my ovary go away. Dr. K's words woke me up and brought me back home to myself. In truth, they brought me back into my most powerful, life-long relationship—the one I have with my body.

Like every woman, I have a complicated relationship with my body. I've swung on the weight pendulum many more times than once. In my twenties, I came dangerously close to embracing anorexia, until my acting coach and mentor Maria Gobetti interrupted that unhealthy pattern. It happened this way—the week before my understudy was to take on my role for the weekend performances, I apologized to Meg, the wardrobe mistress. "I'm sorry to put so much work on you since you are going to have to take in my costume so much for Julie." Meg and Maria looked at me like the RCA logo dog, heads cocked to one side in puzzlement. Meg said, "Dearie, it is quite the opposite. I'm hoping there is enough fabric in the seams to let out so the costumes fit Julie." With that she took the first costume and headed to the sewing machine.

Maria took my hand and led me to the full-length mirror. She stood to the right and just behind me, her hand above the crease of my elbow, her eyes looking at me in the mirror. "What do you see?" she asked. My heart raced. "The fat girl from the spring of my junior year of high school," I said, starting to cry.

For the record, I wasn't fat back then either. Yes, I was curvy and strong and carried 10 pounds of excess on my frame. Yet what I saw in the fun-house mirror in my head was the ongoing comparison to all the petite, non-curvy, popular girls. I lost and gained the same ten pounds countless times since high school. Then, after my father died, I dropped twenty pounds in one month. When I re-entered my life bony, I was flooded with compliments about the new, skinny version of me. I started booking more auditions, callback auditions and roles. It was clear that skinny was what I was "supposed" to be. That day, in 1992, standing in front of that full-length mirror backstage with Maria, I admitted that most days, I thought my size six, five-foot seven-inch version of me was fat.

I felt the heat of shame and embarrassment burn my cheeks. Maria put her left arm around me and locked her eyes full of empathy onto mine in the mirror. She nodded her head as if she knew exactly what I was saying. She guided me over to a pair of chairs and we sat down side by side. "Cry it out," she said with such tenderness, the floodgates opened. I cried over all the lost time focused on the number on the scale. I cried over all the mental, emotional and physical torture I'd doused myself with for so many years. I cried over the hunger pains I ignored. I cried over the self-vitriol based on images force-fed to women by the media. I cried in that theatre dressing room until my tear ducts ran dry.

Later that week I checked out books from the library and read about anorexia, knowing the sensationalized magazine articles would not help me. I did the quizzes in one of the books to determine if I was really in trouble. It turns out no, not in trouble, yet. A tip in one of the books was to plan at least three meals a day, rather than waiting until you were famished to eat. One problem with waiting until you are famished is your stomach can begin to react adversely and you begin to equate eating with hurting. Another tip was to eat when you felt the first pang of hunger, rather than after you experience the adverse effects of hunger like headaches and nausea. I did some version of both and began to understand my body even more. It felt somehow like another layer of the Candida story, but I wasn't clear how just yet.

When I decided to listen to my body, when I decided to partner with her instead of push her or punish her, I discovered that my body partnership was and is an unlimited resource that can guide me in all areas of my life.

The more I listened to my body the more I heard what my relationship with Scott wanted from me—trust, spaciousness, and to bring back my feminine playfulness that he had fallen in love with. The very same things that make me feel most alive. The more I showed my body gentleness, the gentler I treated myself and felt more at ease about how Scott and I were moving forward in our relationship. Well, mostly, and only for a while.

CHAPTER 22

Back to Basics

Knowing I couldn't hand over responsibility for my healing to others, I scribbled in my journal almost every day after the diagnosis, and often three times a day. One morning, I asked, "What is it to live in *this* body right *now?*" The answer was as loud and smart-ass in my head as on the page, "Same as always." The snarky spiritual trickster I call "Om" likes to float around my mind in an enviable full lotus posture, pontificating. She likes to make things overly simple and sometimes, I hate to admit, she's right. I knew her words had merit that morning because, as usual, she reminded me of my simplest solution to most things—meditation.

I put down the pen, closed my eyes and took several deep breaths. I slid into one of my habitual meditations in which I follow an imaginary light beam that emanates from the top of my head, all the way up into the cosmic, astral plane, Milky Way field of Spirit beings. That morning's plug-in connection to the Universe left me, well, tingle-less. Floating among the starry fields, I felt disconcertingly disconnected—from Spirit,

Guides, and my body. With that recognition, I was slammed back into my living room as if kicked out of the warm nest.

"Oh crap, here I go again," I said aloud to the peace lily plant. (I love that it is known for its resilience and forgiving nature.) I'd gotten cocky over all my years of meditating and developed a "shortcut" to connect to the world of Spirit. When I learned to meditate for real in 1993, a lot of attention was placed on connecting to the body first with focused awareness. It helps to calm the mind so that you can more easily plug into that Spirit connection. I had gotten really good at settling my body fast and going straight to that connecting light beam. But given my present state, I clearly needed to honor the basics.

So I placed my hand right between my breasts on my heart chakra and felt my chest rise and fall with my breath. I re-closed my eyes and listened to the rhythm of my heart. I felt the weight of my body on my bum and my feet on the floor. I brought my attention to my heart, and then asked my harmony center (backside of heart chakra) to "please open" and felt the familiar warm wave of harmony rise up inside me.

My inner harmony colors are soft, like the colors in a rainbow just beginning to form. These soft colors feel warm and gentle, almost like a lover's caress. Harmony circulated up my spine into my head, then down into my left shoulder and arm, down my left rib cage, waist, hips and leg. Next, this rainbow light of harmony moved down my right shoulder, arm, chest, waist, hip and leg. It radiated into my organs and veins, muscles and bones. My body absorbed it, inflating me with life in the way my peace lily plant expands when I water it after being away for a week.

I then turned my attention onto my skin. What did I sense there? Could I feel the breeze coming in the window? What did the air feel like entering my nose? I did a body scan to check for tightness in my neck, shoulders, hips and even my facial muscles. It was like a morning status check. It felt comfortingly familiar, like waking up in my grandparent's house to the smell of sizzling bacon and fresh coffee. I was coming home, into the home of my body.

"Bloody hell. I've lived outside of my body for at least six months." It was so clear to me as I sat in the stillness after meditating. Was this a conscious decision, I wondered? No. It was just my way of coping. My body's fertility messages, and my glacial-moving love relationship were just too painful or scary to heed. Plus, just like I'd gotten cocky with meditation, I'd gotten cocky as a coach. I'd forgotten the old adage, "Physician, heal thyself." I wasn't taking care of my own emotional and physical needs nor was I currently being coached, despite knowing better. Result: each month that ticked by ratcheted up my panic level. It was like I was on some twisted countdown and I kept reaching zero though there wasn't even a shuttle on the pad for lift-off, or in my case, an embryo.

There it is, I thought. The culprit was the hidden dragon that the crouching tiger tried to protect me from knowing. Every time I saw a baby, my lower stomach, OK, my uterus, contracted and every cell of me ached to hold my newborn. Because I couldn't scream out loud my pain every time I saw a stroller or a child's eyes locked on mine, I imploded on the inside.

Ohhh no. Had I become that god-forsaken character Lauren from the play *Stopping the Desert*? Whose sole intent was to be a mom, and who became more and more panicky and morose with each month's start of her period?

When I understudied Lauren in my late twenties, the female lead character, I dove into crafting the character like I could be called to the stage at any moment (which I often was). In one brief scene, she wanders into a pool of light mid-stage, wrapped in a decidedly unsexy terry-cloth housecoat. Her husband asks, "What's wrong?" She announces in a numb monotone, "I'm bleeding." He puts his arms around her dutifully, without love, without empathy, and without really embracing her, and then the lights slowly fade to black. Next scene? He's having an affair with sexy, carefree Nina and planning to leave Lauren.

Recoiling from the memory of Lauren, I burst into tears, feeling my own panic ratchet into Lauren-like full-blown anxiety. I habitually took on the nuances of my characters, as when I felt desperate and depressed when I played Marilyn Monroe in *After the Fall* by Arthur Miller and felt feline slinky sexy after taking on Maggie in *Cat on a Hot Tin Roof*. Had I taken on Lauren's miserable childless fate? I leapt off the sofa and paced around my condo, almost carving a path in the carpet pile as I moved in figure eights around the living room and dining room table like a caged animal. Had I become Lauren? Weren't my own life's twists and turns enough—did I have to bring in extra drama?

I was taught in my college freshman acting class, and then again later in acting classes in L.A., to fantasize about the early life of a character. The best way to fantasize is to actually feel the scenarios rather than simply imagining them. So I'd place my whole body into the scene and see it happening in first person. I'd look down and see the front of my body and arm reaching out to open a door, just like I do in real life, rather than see my entire body from a distance as if on a movie screen. The theory is fantasizing about characters' lives this way makes them more real, therefore believable on stage. And so, when I work with clients, I employ the very same tactics in having them visualize the life they want to be living.

Called into examining the possibility that Lauren's character still lived inside me, I grabbed my journal again and wrote very slowly, "Whose life am I living?" and then in huge letters; "NOT Lauren's." I closed my eyes and imagined an eraser scrubbing away the last vestiges of Lauren's character. The eraser started in my head, erasing the character's thoughts. Moving into my heart, the eraser swiped away Lauren's forlorn bitterness. Next, the eraser moved to my ovaries, erasing whatever Lauren's fertility issues were. The eraser circled around me, dusting off the external connections to other characters. Finally, the eraser returned to my head for another erasing of Lauren's thoughts.

"If I'm not Lauren, Marilyn or any other character I've ever inhabited on the stage, and I'm not my mother or her version of what she dreamed my life would be, and I'm not in the mama role yet, who am I?"

JoyFullLight, my wise Future Self popped in and said, "Darling, your authentic self lives in your body, thrives on connection to Spirit and intuition, is divinely feminine and is now reclaiming being of service to *herself* as much as she is to others. You've just drifted. Get busy living in your body."

"I'm scared to. I feel people's words, what they don't say, my emotions, my words, what I don't say . . . I feel it all in my body. I'm tired of processing it all through my body," I admitted.

"What better way to know the truth?" she asked before heading back to the future.

Am I ready for more truth? Am I ready to again listen to what the sweaty palms, tight shoulders, clogged throat, and upset stomach signals reveal? Despite all the progress I had made inside the healing circle and with Dr. S, I was still scared to hear and heed the message of my ovary. What might it be trying to tell me? "What if your ovary has good things to tell you, Cat?" I asked with all the positivity I could muster. And what if that "good" thing is something I don't want to hear . . . like I really did wait until too late?

Tired and not quite ready for more internal dialog, I reopened my journal and practiced again the philosophy of "intention and attention" and wrote out *what I wanted* my ovary to be telling me. Things like: "Healing is the way to go!" And, "You are doing all the right, smart things!" And, daddy's imperative, "Receive love." And, from my Tinkerbelle souvenir t-shirt message, "Believe!"

CHAPTER 23

It's All About the Eyes

I was calm when I walked into Dr. K's office for the pre-op appointment, the result of listening to a Sanskrit chant CD on the hour-long Friday morning commute. I felt certain I would not need surgery the following week. Even the waiting room, filled with patients flipping magazine pages, didn't faze me.

I signed in, catching the eye of the bespectacled gal who runs the office. She's the kind you are always glad is there. Clearly overqualified for this job, yet she remains year after year. I want to ask her about the bold-framed glasses, but don't. Hands on the computer keyboard, phone to her ear, she nevertheless heard me as I asked about a pre-op urine sample. She nodded then pointed her head in the direction of the restroom as she continued typing, still talking with a patient on the phone.

I returned to the waiting room and sat down in my favorite chair, thinking how weirdly comforting it is to have a favorite chair in a doctor's waiting room. My back to one wall, I could see the main door and the reception window. I looked at the couple sitting on the couch to my right, holding hands and taking turns flipping pages of the same magazine. Definitely a fertility couple, I thought. The woman opposite the magazine and toy-strewn table in front of me hadn't looked up from her Ayn Rand book once. I think she read the same two pages the entire fifteen minutes I sat there.

I opened my journal and began writing the scene I had envisioned and rehearsed during my daily visualization and meditation since hearing I needed surgery. My pen sped across the paper, propelled by my need to finish writing out the scene before my name was called. I wrote three pages, detailing exactly how I wanted the meeting with the doctor to play out, including the words I wanted to hear from Dr. K.

I finished reviewing the pages and felt gratitude flow through my body, warm and comforting, just as the nurse called my name. I was calm, serene, almost. The nurse checked my vitals, and we both smiled at my low blood pressure. She led me to the exam room and said all the usual things, "Undress from the waist down, cover your lower half with this; the doctor will be in momentarily." I casually folded my jeans and panties and put them on the rounded plastic chair and then covered myself with the large piece of baby-blue paper called a sheet. Settling onto the cushioned, and yet slightly uncomfortable exam table, I turned off the glaring over-head fluorescent light, lay back, closed my eyes, and visualized my desired scenario once more.

I inhaled a slow, deep cleansing breath then exhaled fully, thinking of the Latin term, exspiritus. Inhale again—inspiritus. Exhale again—exspiritus. I invited JoyFullLight to join me, and my Guardian Angel, Glinda, who looks like Billy Burke from *The Wizard of Oz*, though sounds like she's from Atlanta, Georgia rather than Munchkinland. I also called in my go-to Goddesses of Healing, Persephone and Kuan Yin. Next, I envisioned a pulsating, multi-colored healing energy bonfire and when it appeared, I stepped inside it, experiencing its warmth and light in my solar plexus. The pulsating energy surged up and through my chakras. I directed the energy to my right ovary and felt the tingling twitch of healing. I envisioned the doctor looking at the ultrasound and saying with glee and amazement, "You did it! The growth is gone! Your ovary is clear and pink and beautiful!"

Just as I brought my visualization to a close, Dr. K knocked lightly on the door and came in. "How are you feeling?" she asked, leaving the fluorescent overhead light off.

"Good," I said with confidence.

We chitchatted about my trip to Disneyland while she typed her password into the exam room laptop. Then I told her about the healing ceremony, phone session with the naturopathic doctor, shifting my diet to be more alkaline, claiming, "I think it's gone!"

"Let's see," she said rather flatly. I'd heard my father's similar tone when talking to patients on the phone. Kind of a "never over-promise and always try to over-deliver" vibe.

She covered and lubed up the ultrasound wand, and slowly inserted it into my vagina. She furrowed her brow a little as she looked at the screen and then moved the wand to the left.

"Just breathe, Cat," I told myself and practiced breathing in Latin: inspiritus, exspiritus.

Looking at the ultrasound monitor she said, "Right side, right?" and I said, "Yes." Her fingers clicked across the keyboard and I heard the machine take a picture.

I saw a slow smile spread all the way up to her eyes, just like she had in my forty-one visualizations. She turned from the monitor and looked into my eyes with her big smile.

"It shrunk! It's less than half the size it was! No surgery for you!" I exhaled then began laughing my gratitude, like a schoolgirl being told a bawdy joke that she had already heard.

Dr. K jumped back into detail land, explaining just how much smaller the growth was (from seven plus centimeters down to three centimeters), and confirmed the surgery would be cancelled. "Come back for a follow-up after your next cycle." My gratitude got lost in all the details, replaced by a startled look. Dr. K noticed and puzzled, said, "This is *great* news! Where's that smile gone?"

I gave her a command performance smile, but wondered how there could be anything left of the growth after Daddy said it was fine. I assumed Daddy meant he *removed* the entire growth. And then I got it: Daddy was on my healing team . . . not my surgical team! As if following Dr. K's directive, I smiled for real.

"Keep doing whatever it is you are doing, it's working!" She paused for a few moments, as if carefully choosing her next words. "It still looks tissue filled, but it . . . I know I'm not supposed to say things like this, but you're a surgeon's kid—it doesn't *seem* like cancer because this kind of cancer grows. It just doesn't shrink like this." I liked how Dr. K smiled at me as she left the room. I felt somehow like a "good" patient and that I was in the club.

On my way out of the office, my favorite bespectacled gal said, "This is a good day! Any day we get to cancel a surgery is a good day!" The relief in her voice reflected my own.

"I couldn't agree more," I said, looking toward the heavens with thanks.

Back in my car, I placed my hands on the steering wheel and leaned my head on them, whispering a string of gratitude to the Spirit world, to my lovely healing goddesses, to Daddy, and to all the people who prayed for and sent healing energy my way. I didn't realize I was crying until a tear landed on my arm and ran down to the crease of my bent elbow. I sat upright and caught a glimpse of my gratitude-filled face in the rear-view mirror. It looked softer than my reflection of a few short weeks prior.

I felt like what had just taken place was an old-fashioned miracle. The kind that transpires when I show up and participate in my spiritual, mental and emotional healing. "Receive Love. Yes, please, and thank you! I will continue to do so," I thought, looking forward to the rest of that day's healing activities.

CHAPTER 24

The Akashic Records - You Can Look it Up!

What woman doesn't love the opportunity to dress up, sip champagne while savoring morsels of cake and use curling ribbon on gift bags? My girlfriends are no different. So I hoped I wouldn't disappoint them when I decided to forego the usual champagne birthday toasts, choosing instead to accept their love and good wishes via another healing circle.

One goddess-sister-friend, Barb, offered to facilitate an Akashic Records reading for my birthday, offering a time to meet a few hours before the healing circle.

"Heck yeah!" I said, when Barb made the suggestion. Barb entered the Modern Goddess fold when she contacted me after reading an ad calling for mentees, which I'd posted with my mentor Diane Miller in the Women In Theatre newsletter. We needed help to run the Outreach program and promised takers they'd learn about the feminine way of mentoring and supporting other women that Diane and I had honed. Though about ten years older than I am, Barb said she wanted to learn about feminine Goddess energies to balance out all the doing, doing, doing in the masculine-dominated business she was involved in. After attending my Modern Goddess workshop and a few full moon ceremonies, she was all in!

The Akashic Records are like a Google search of life and karma held on servers in the Spirit world. Based on Hindu tradition, the records contain major events, people, wisdom and dreams of our previous, current and future lives. What I love about the concept is anyone can learn to access them through guidance, deep meditation and a willingness to see beyond the earthly realm.

I'd never had my Akashic Records read out loud to me, though a Pranic healer once said she removed previous life wounds showing up in this life's body after looking at my Akashic Records. She also told me my etheric body still contained my right kidney. (I was still very new to alternative forms of healing when I lay on the Pranic healer's table. Even though that surgeon's daughter part of me was trying to roll her eyes in scientific skepticism, I believed the healer because I could feel the truth of her words inside my body.)

Since I'd already encountered my father in spirit form while in yoga's Child's Pose, received a laying on of hands in my healing circle, mashed around my internal organs with Vaishali, and cleared leftover anger, grief and sadness over the phone with Dr. S, having an Akashic Records reading felt like the next "logical" step, or one more piece of spaghetti on my refrigerator door.

I parked in front of Barb's house exactly where I'd parked each full moon during the late 1990's. She loved my full moon ceremonies so much she offered her backyard when the circle grew so large it was hard for us all to fit in my apartment's living room. Many of our circles had more than 30 people and those ceremonies had two circles, one inside the other one! Getting out of my car, I whispered a prayer of gratitude for Barb and her husband Glenn's generous offering of their backyard sanctuary to the Modern Goddesses.

A sense of home-like familiarity swept through me as I walked through the driveway gate past the kitchen door to the edge of the grass. I stood motionless and breathed in the backyard, still smelling of the ceremonial sage and cedar bundles we used to purify our thoughts before a ceremony. Glenn runs a Native American sweat lodge in the backyard, and the Spirit vibrations are very high. Though the thirteen-foot tall tipi where we sat in circle for so many years is no longer there, I felt its energy welcoming me like a friendly ghost. "Thank you for all the magic," I mouthed silently to the trees that encircled the space where the tipi once stood. Though no longer living, I sensed the presence of Ginger (a dachshund) and Wolf, (part German Shepherd and wild wolf). The two of them bounded up to greet me each full moon as soon as I walked in the gate. I breathed in the backyard again and felt gratitude settle over me. This had been a beautiful home for our ceremonies until Rich and I moved from the apartment, and our own beautiful backyard became the gathering spot.

When I turned toward the house, Barb was coming down the backdoor steps.

"If anyone could do it, I knew you could," she said, celebrating my good news. During my prior healing ceremony, I hadn't noticed that her salt and pepper hair was cropped much shorter now, and there was a new contentment about her. How did I miss these things? Perhaps I'd been more into receive-mode than I realized.

We settled into her home office, sipping green tea from brown stoneware mugs that felt comfortingly warm as I wrapped both hands around mine. Barb sat at her desk under the window facing the circle drive, and I tried to lounge in the formal side chair next to the desk, facing her. As she arranged her papers of Akashic Records maps, she asked what else I'd been doing to heal my ovary. I shared my experiences with Dr. S, listening to Vaishali, daily meditation and visualization, and my visit from Daddy.

She nodded, eyes twinkling and said, "Perfect! Ready to get started?" I nodded my yes. "Great! We'll open with a prayer of intention and ask permission to access your records then I'll guide you through a meditation that will move us from the earthly plane of consciousness to higher realms of Spirit consciousness. From there, I'll read what is shown me in the Records. You can ask questions, too," she said, knowing I would want to.

At Barb's direction, I closed my eyes. On a deep exhale, a space inside me began to open up and my neck seemed to lengthen as my shoulders relaxed. She began the prayer and I silently invoked Glinda, my Guardian Angel, to accompany me on the journey. She instantly appeared by my side, whispering, "Let go; your only job is to trust Barb and the process." Once again on this healing journey, I surrendered my daily role of being the guide for others, and slipped into the world of the visualization.

At Barb's direction, I inhaled and exhaled slowly. She invited me to allow my body to soften by breathing into any physical tightness or discomfort I felt. With each exhale, I was directed to imagine the tightness unwinding. As I relaxed, my body opened, and she either saw or sensed the opening and asked me to shift my attention from my body to my third eye chakra (middle of the forehead), inviting me to connect with Spirit through that portal. She said we were entering into a space where linear time didn't exist. As she continued with the Akashic prayer, I found myself in spacious spirals of shimmering purple energy, like sparkly gossamer. It enveloped me like fabric, slightly protective. I reached out to touch it; it felt like a rush of air. I liked it. Maybe this is what Chaub, my beloved golden retriever had experienced, ears blowing in the wind when he stuck his head out of the car window. The purple field gave way to a sheer gold light as Barb guided me into ever more spaciousness far away from the earthly plane. I was floating yet held in a tender embrace.

Once we reached the plane of the Akashic Records, Barb whispered, "Your father is here."

I had seen him drifting toward me just before she spoke. No longer wearing the khaki green fishing jumpsuit he sported when I encountered him last, he was dressed in his trademark green scrubs. My mom was half-convinced his eyes were green because they always looked green when he wore those scrubs. I'm convinced his eyes were like a mood ring. I knew to stay out of his way when his eyes turned grey. And there in the Akashic Records, my hazel eyes locked onto his blue ones, and he smiled at me.

"Forgiveness is here," Barb said quietly. I found myself nodding, both at my father and at his message. Forgiveness was what had begun to wind itself through me with each of my healing experiences.

"Forgive yourself, Cat. We did our best," said Daddy, clearing emotion from his throat after he spoke, like he did when filled with nostalgia and longing after telling a story about his childhood experiences with his own father. Before I could ask him any questions about this round of forgiveness, the swirls of sheer gold swept around him and he faded into their fold. I wanted to run after him. I wanted more of his presence. I wanted more of his forgiveness to help me own mine. More than anything, I wanted him to not have died. There is no chasing or running after in the Akashic Records field—only a sense of floating, suspended energy.

Next, Rich floated into view. Barb said the Records revealed that the karmic connection he and I have has been expressed through multiple lifetimes. I suppressed the urge to say, "I know."

"You will know him forever," my inner voice whispered on that October night in 1990 when we met at The Hollywood Athletic Club during my first night as a cocktail waitress. Over the din of loud music and the clank of pool balls dropping into pockets, I recognized his voice in my heart.

Barb's voice jostled me from my reverie as she relayed the next message from the Records: Rich and I had completed the task of this lifetime's karmic lesson. A wild mix of relief, sadness and wonder bounced between my chest and stomach. And then curiosity —we were supposed to wind up like this? I tried to make sense of that thought and couldn't.

She moved on to my current love, Scott, and said, "He is a good man with a good heart." Yes, a very good man with a very good heart, I repeated inside myself. "He loves you, truly," she said.

Even though I know the Akashic Records provide insight and context and are not a best-selling "how-to" manual for life's problems, I had been secretly hoping for a message or action plan. I wanted to leapfrog beyond my ovarian circumstance of the moment to a more certain future. More than that, I fantasized that the Records would wave a magic wand and whisper, "You've done enough soul-lesson work in this lifetime. From here on out, all you have to do is enjoy life!"

Barb asked if I had any questions.

"Will I be able to get pregnant?" rushed out of my mouth like a pent-up river when a dam is opened.

We sat in silence for a moment and then Barb said, "The journey to pregnancy and motherhood will be challenging . . . though not impossible. The Records say balancing your hormones will be key."

"What does that mean?" I wondered aloud.

I don't remember what happened in the Records after that. The next thing I do remember is Barb guiding me back through the gold and purple swirls of cosmic light, letting me linger in the soothing softness. When I opened my eyes, the room seemed overly bright, despite the slanted window blinds. I took a few deep breaths and rotated my wrists and ankles. In an attempt to feel more grounded, I took a sip of tepid green tea and snacked on a few almonds I had stashed in a Ziploc bag in my purse. Each time I opened or closed a Ziploc bag, I couldn't help but see the image Dr. K's words painted, the growth neatly bagged.

Barb and I sat in silence for a few moments before both of us went into "coach" mode and brainstormed possible ways I could move forward, creating balance in my hormones and indeed my life. The question running on loop in my head was, "Is my lifetime of imbalance going to haunt me?"

In one of those "life before your eyes" moments, scenes of my life flashed through my head. I heard my mother's loving voice calmly explaining one of my five-year-old, roller coaster moments to my brother. "It's always the highest of the highs and the lowest of the lows with your sister. We just saw a deaf man outside the store. He gave her that little rose. She didn't know that he was asking for money in exchange for the rose, or that he was deaf until we were on the highway and I told her what the slip of paper said. She wanted to go back and I didn't. She's been crying and mad at me ever since."

"You won't ever be able to eat sugar, yeast, flour, fermented foods or chemical preservatives like other people can," said the alternative MD after my grueling, yearlong recovery from systemic Candida. "You have to choose: birthday cake or a glass of champagne. Not both." I was twenty-seven years old.

From wild child who ate and drank everything to a Spartan living on rice cakes, salad greens and water. Maybe it all fits my Aries personality of . . . a little excess.

"Trying to find balance seems to be the theme of my life," I muttered between heartfelt thanks as I hugged Barb goodbye. Meditation taught me the art of detachment, or how not to take things personally. Tapping into my feminine energy and honoring the priestess within taught me how to balance my hard driving, masculine achiever energy with my go-with-the-flow serenity. Becoming a coach taught me to be curious rather than judgmental and to experience more inner peace. And now, I was being invited to find even more balance through my body, and specifically my hormones.

I got in my car and suddenly had one of those "right with the Universe" moments, knowing I was in exactly the right place, at exactly the right time, seeking exactly the right support for my journey on Earth. Even though I was still *slightly* cursing the "opportunity" to learn about balance again.

CHAPTER 25

Insurance

My "insurance" healing chamber gathered at Veronica's that night at 7:00 o'clock. Most of my healers were part of the first circle, and two others were able to join this one. Following my lead to stay tranquil and not engage in too much raucous conversation, my goddess-sisters circled around me quietly. As she had done twelve days before, Veronica placed a folded-in-half-lengthwise comforter on the living room floor to signal the beginning, and complete calm ensued. My goddess-sisters placed pillows under my neck and knees making me feel pampered. As each intentionally chose where to sit, according to which part of my body they were drawn to support, they were transformed into healers. I noticed a negotiation of sorts as two of the goddesses partnered up sitting next to each other on my left side. I nodded "yes" when a red fleece blanket was offered. Ever so gently it was draped over my legs.

Feeling nestled in the circle I smiled up at them. "Dr. K said no surgery!"

"Oh, Kitty Cat—YAY," said Tamara, clapping her hands. "Of *course* you don't have to have surgery," said Kiyomi, laughing and squeezing my hand. I allowed the glee in their eyes and love to wash through me.

"The growth is shrinking and is just less than half the size it was. Dr. K said I should keep doing whatever it is I'm doing, which is why we are all here tonight!"

I continued, "Barb led me through an Akashic Records reading earlier this afternoon," and my healers all turned toward Barb, acknowledging her gift. "The big message is balance. Please focus your energy on the *complete* disappearance of the growth and that my body finds balance." Catching my Chief Operating Officer of Control mask sneaking in, very slowly and with full intention I said, "I ask for divine wisdom and healing to occur." Then I closed my eyes to indicate my part of the invocation was complete.

After a moment, Tamara began: "We are here for Cat's highest good and healing. We come together in love and support. May we be instruments for divine healing, love and perfect health, for Cat and the rest of us too."

Just as I mouthed, "Blessed be," I heard whispers of "And so it is," and "Blessed be."

In the silence that followed, I felt my healers connect with their own Guides. Even with my eyes closed, I knew from familiarity that a few had their hands folded together in a "Namaste" position in front of their hearts, and that still others rested their hands gently on their knees. I invited Glinda my Guardian Angel, JoyFullLight my Future Self, and the rest of my posse of Guides and Angels to join in the fun. "We live for this kind of support of you, darling!" drawled Glinda. The rest of my inner guide team created a bit of a party atmosphere around me.

I felt my healers' warm, energized-with-love hands approach my body. I breathed deeper into my relaxation. In my mind's eye, I tried to find the purple and gold swirl of energy I floated in earlier that afternoon. Instead I floated into what felt like an ocean of stars. My lungs expanded fully and my stomach rose with the depth of the breath. I melted into the floor a little on that exhale.

My attention shifted to the center of my chest when four hot hands channeled what I can only call a vigorous, fiery energy into my heart chakra. It felt like they were stirring soup with a giant spoon in the middle of my chest.

Next, my attention flowed to the widening sensation in my pelvic area when someone rhythmically yet very gently tapped on my right ovary. I felt a dark brown swirl of energy rush out of my ovary as the tapping hand shifted to "plucking" on my ovary. It felt like the leftovers, the held-onto emotions in my heart's refrigerator and examined with Dr. S, were now being released from my ovary. Those emotions had turned into stuck energy and had formed the growth. And now they were streaming out of me. I didn't feel compelled to name them again; I just let them go.

"Trust," floated through my brain. I was experiencing a deep state of trust in my goddess-sisters. I trusted their intentions, their wisdom, their healing efforts and their love of me. I melted further into the experience, losing the sensation of distinct body parts. I began to feel as if everything in me and around me was operating as a unit of some kind. In that wondrous moment, the individual parts merged with the elements of the infinite.

I returned to my body from the cosmic zone when Kiyomi, a part-time Pilates instructor, whispered in my left ear, "Inhale deeply." Upon my breath's exhale she squeezed my ribs together to assist the release of "stale" air.

"Kitty Cat, you aren't fully exhaling," she said gently. "Really let it go. Ready?"

I nodded and followed her directions. With each slow exhale she squeezed my ribcage gently from each side. It felt like my baseboards were being vacuumed after years of not being cleaned. With each timed, slow inhale I could feel more air and energy in my lungs, and more space with each exhale.

Just as I was becoming lightheaded with all the oxygen, she whispered in my right ear, "Turn over." I could barely move, but managed with her help to slowly turn myself over. The pillow that had been under my knees was placed under my ankles. There seemed to be one thousand hands on my mid back, right at heart level, right where my father's Spirit had placed his hand four days before. I felt and saw two channels open where my healer's hands rested. One channel released streams of dark looking energy and the other received translucent white and electric blue energy. I imagined closing the door to my linear mind and focused solely on the energy sensations, continuing to inhale and exhale.

Inhale to a count of four, hold for a count of four, exhale to a count of four and hold for a count of four. My chiropractor calls this controlled breath. I call it the 4x4. I found myself organically breathing in this manner after Kiyomi released the stale air in my lungs, and as I lay on my stomach.

"Child's Pose" was the direction from one of my Guides. Moving very slowly, I folded my legs beneath me, the tops of my feet on the floor, the backs of my thighs resting on the back of my calves. In slow motion, I curled my chest onto my thighs, arms next to my legs, and my forehead eased onto the floor.

I experienced my breath as a healing "dance" when Kiyomi gently stretched my back forward to the rhythm of each breath. With each exhale, more hands joined to stretch my back ever so slightly, taking me further into the reach of Child's Pose.

I dissolved into a trance-like state and experienced what I can only describe as merging into the soup of the Universe. I had no boundary or form of a body, only energy. There was no linear time in this transcendent state, so it didn't matter whether I'd been there for five seconds, five minutes, five hours, or five days. In this suspended state, I experienced the release of grief and sorrow from more than just this lifetime. I felt like I was being re-birthed.

When my consciousness merged back into flesh and bone, my healer's hands were no longer over me. I sensed them in meditation and prayer and imagined them holding hands to maintain the energy in the circle. I unfolded my body from child's pose and very slowly turned onto my back. Someone draped the fleece blanket over me.

I became aware of the tears flowing from the outside corners of my eyes, rolling across my temples into my hair. "Ancient tears" said one of my Guides. No external drama or hysteria required for the release. The deep love of my dear friends gently dismantled the dam and my tears flowed like an unhurried spring rain.

I believe all the aircraft pilots that took off from the Burbank airport and flew over Veronica's home in Studio City that evening, witnessed a very bright light emanating from her roof. Now, whether they understood what the light meant is another matter!

How often do we truly comprehend what is really happening in the moment?

CHAPTER 26

Funky & Forty-Five

I knew it would be at once different and exactly the same. This was the one-month follow-up and I was calm when I entered Dr. K's waiting room. I had just come from a casual banter at the Starbuck's across the street. "Yes, decaf in the morning," I joked with the barista. The too-pretty-to-be-anything-but-a-model-actor young man, half my age, smiled his flirt at me for no apparent reason. I tossed my hair as I coyly shared my appreciation with a half-curled lip and one arched eyebrow. The woman behind me in line visibly thought, "cougar", so I winked at her!

Dr. K's waiting room was empty and the gals behind the desk, whom I know a little too well now, waved and smiled when I walked in. I chose the couch this time because the bold tabloid headline facing the couch was "Jen pregnant at last!" I was drawn in by Jennifer Anniston's radiant smile. I took a deep breath and imagined my smiling face at three months pregnant looking just as glowing, smooth and airbrushed! *(Note: the headline turned out to be a rumor, but it drew me in, and I wanted to believe "pregnant at last" was possible for both of us. Over the years since, I think I've seen a similar headline for her another half dozen times.)*

I didn't touch the magazine, just let Jen's smile do all the talking. I knew what that smile would feel like when I smiled it. I had a knowing deep inside me of what it would feel like to rub my stomach and soothe a kicking fetus. I had joked with a colleague just recently, "I will be so thrilled when pregnant that I'll want people to feel my stomach as my baby moves. I'll run around shouting, 'The baby is moving, the baby is moving! Here, feel it,' to all in my vicinity."

"Mary?" the seemingly dis-embodied-looking head asked, the rest of the aide's body hidden behind the door. I had explained to the new aide during my last visit that my insurance name is Mary, but I go by Cat. "OK," she had said blandly, not making a physical or mental note. The nurse entered the exam room, and I was led through all the obligatory vital signs.

Once again, I lay beneath the baby-blue paper sheet, just as I had thirty-one days prior. I envisioned Dr. K looking at the ultrasound screen exclaiming, "Yippee, it's gone!" I had envisioned this scenario at least 100 times in the last 31 days. I could feel myself smiling as I heard Dr. K's fast walk coming toward me on the wood hallway floor.

She smiled and laughed softly when she walked in, casting her eyes to the dark ceiling. "How long have you been in here? Hopefully not long enough for a nap! I'm sorry about the wait. I got backed up early this morning."

"No, just meditating," I said. She smiled again, nodding her head approvingly as she slipped a condom over the ultrasound wand, lubed it with gel and casually inserted it into me.

We both looked at the monitor, she at the screen and me the side of it.

"Left side, right?"

"Right side," I said, noticing her furrowed brow.

Back and forth went the wand, tiny jabs each time. I watched her furrowed brow. Silently, she looked at the screen, moving the probe back and forth again.

"Ouch!" I flinched.

"Oh, Cat, I'm so sorry. I just, I'm just trying to see, to see . . ." And then, after a few more gentle back and forth movements of the wand she said, "The right side is clear." Before I could shout "Hallelujah!" she added, "Your right ovary is about to release an egg and I see what looks like a very tiny cyst developing on your left ovary."

I felt the tears spill from the outside corners of my eyes and roll down into my hair as I lounged back, joyful to the bone at the words, "the right side is clear!" and "release an egg."

She kept talking as she printed the image scans from the ultrasound machine and paper-clipped them to my file before entering who knows what into her exam room laptop.

"You're just forty-five and funky. Let's watch this thing on your left ovary because that last growth raised some alarms. What we would normally do is put you on birth control pills, but," she trailed off not needing to state the obvious.

S-L-O-W-D-O-W-N, how can this seem like a furrowed-brow problem? I'm ovulating each month, for chrissake, my brain screamed. Dr. K's reaction indicated there was something to be handled.

I sat up with the baby-blue paper sheet wrapped around my lower half, and waited for the keyboard clicking to stop.

"Come back in the middle of your next cycle," Dr. K said, closing her laptop.

"I won't be here. I fly to Toronto on Saturday for two weeks for work, from there I head to New Orleans via Texas for my brother's wedding festivities for another two weeks."

"Well, have fun, come back in two months and we'll look again. If there are any growths present then we will decide what to do at that time." She gathered up my chart and smiled at me as she paused in the doorway. "This looks okay. You're just forty-five and funky," she repeated.

"Thanks," I said with an upward inflection as the door clicked closed.

I sat there, beginning to question the glee I felt. I was confounded by Dr. K's *lack* of glee. I wanted her to celebrate with me like she had when the growth on my right ovary first shrunk. I wanted her to tell me that my dietary shifts and deep inner healing work had paid off. I wanted a pat of approval on my head. I wanted some kind of acknowledgment of what I felt was a magical journey of healing. Most of all, I wanted her to say, "Yes, you can still make babies!"

I could hear her brisk heeltaps up and down the hallway, as I got dressed. Buttoning my blouse, I wondered what was wrong with me that I didn't see the potential problem she clearly anticipated. Would each ovulation produce a cyst or growth of some kind? Would repeated growths lead to cancer? Looking at the poster for fertility treatments on the wall, I heard the fear-filled question: Was I delusional about my possibility of becoming pregnant without the IVF assistance? Assistance I'd already decided was not for me. I'd wondered for years if too much scar tissue had formed from too many cysts on my right ovary, preventing the release of eggs. Yet she had just said it was releasing an egg!

Reaching for my very best Pollyanna positivity and my purse, I tried to shake my head free of negative thoughts. "She just said my right ovary was releasing an egg!" I repeated under my breath, deciding to focus on the fact that *both* ovaries were still working. I can live with forty-five and funky if forty-five and funky means ovulation I decided. I called Scott as soon as I got in the car.

CHAPTER 27

Face to Face

I could almost feel the indentations from the millions of arms that had rested on the well-worn counter of the diner in downtown Toronto. The lone waitress, a stocky, middle-aged, bottle-platinum blonde took my order in English with a pronounced Eastern European accent. She looked disapproving when I told her I didn't want the bacon or sausage included in the breakfast, and she seemed almost hurt when I declined the toast. She gave my order to the fry cook whose white apron sported a diagonal hand swipe of grease from just below his left chest. The raised eyebrows, arm gestures, and grunts that flew between them told the story of a complicated and monotonous relationship.

The scrambled eggs and hash browns were as perfect as I knew they would be in an old-style breakfast diner . . . the eggs a touch underdone and the hash browns crunchy on the top and bottom. I wondered if Dr. S was going to tell me not to eat such things when I saw her in person. And I wondered if she, like most other alternative healers I'd ever been to, would tell me to stop drinking my beloved coffee. At that fearsome thought, I took a slow sip and savored the surprisingly good brew.

I was in Toronto to facilitate a two-day leadership training for one client, and a three-day coach training for another client, and had decided to take the opportunity to have a session with Dr. S in person. Rather than have me visit her clinic, which was on the other side of the city from where I was staying, Dr. S invited me to meet her at the Verity Women's Club where she was a member. I walked the few short blocks from the diner to the club to be greeted by a mix of glossy-wood paneled country club, luxury spa, and big deals going down over breakfast. As I signed my name in the guest book, I received a text from Dr. S letting me know she would be a bit late.

A stylish, mini-skirted young woman led me to the lounge area. Before I had taken off my coat and settled into the sofa, she brought coffee in a formal cup and saucer set-up, a glass of water with a floating, thin lemon slice and the morning newspaper. I had the feeling if I asked her for slippers, I might just get them. Flipping through the Toronto paper, more for distraction than to catch up on the news, I mused on why L.A. didn't have a women's club like this. Momentarily enchanted by thoughts of creating such a place, it hit me: Why can't all Western medicine's doctors' waiting rooms be like this? Cozy, private, warm, full beverage service including pastries - now that would get us to annual check-ups!

Just as I placed my empty coffee cup on its saucer, the mini-skirted young woman appeared. Her arrival was so timely, I wondered if she'd been watching me.

"Dr. S phoned and will be here shortly. Would you like to follow me to your meeting room?"

I gathered my coat and bags and said, "Sure."

She walked rather quickly, but I sauntered, peering into each open door we passed. The conference rooms looked boringly normal with the obligatory giant oval table and high backed, high-end leather office chairs. I had been hoping to see a conference room full of chaise lounges and robes ready to replace suit jackets!

The smaller "sitting" rooms were more like my fantasy. Each one had a different jewel-tone on the walls, tapestry or velvet covered wing chairs and soft-looking sofas. No white sterile walls, low-to-the-ground rolling stools or stirrup exam tables here.

The young woman abruptly stopped and opened the door to one of the small sitting rooms. I wanted to touch the textured rich ruby wallpaper, noting the ruby red was brighter than the deep Spanish red color on my kitchen walls at home.

"Dr. S will be here shortly. May I bring you more coffee?" the young woman asked.

As much as I wanted the warmth and comfort of another cup, I declined, lifting my water bottle from my bag for her to see.

I made myself at home on the deep marine-blue velvet covered sofa, slipping off my boots and folding into my favorite crossed-legged meditation position. "Ah, no overhead fluorescent lights, only table lamps," I said aloud. I couldn't help comparing the environment of this doctor visit with the ones I'd had in L.A. with Dr. K. Of course, this charming room was not really Dr. S's office, so the comparison was unfair. And yet, it highlighted how lacking in charm and comfort most exam rooms are.

I re-focused and took three slow breaths and invited a harmonious flow of energy from my heart-center to fill up my body. I felt the tingling, energetic waves radiate from my chest up into my head, down my arms, torso and legs. When the harmonious energy reached my toes, the door opened, as if on cue.

"Cat, I'm so sorry to be late. I really don't like to rush my work with patients and my last session ran over," said Dr. S immediately upon entering. I smiled and nodded, knowing I had received extra time with her in our previous session. She draped her coat and bag over one of the two wingback tapestry covered chairs and opened her arms wide to give me a hug.

Dr. S is a petite, no, a tinier than petite, woman. My five feet seven inches towered over her as we hugged each other like old friends. Feeling downright Amazonian, I was momentarily discombobulated because I had made up that Dr. S would be tall, have wild curly hair and wear Birkenstock sandals like so many California naturopathic doctors I'd encountered. What other assumptions would prove to be wrong?

Her dark straight hair glinted in the low lamplight and I wondered what conditioner she used. My mind chatter began. "She eats for nourishment rather than pleasure or emotional salve. In fact, Cat, that shiny hair is probably from a lack of coffee and salty-crunchy things." I closed my eyes intentionally to banish the voice of the Perfectionista.

She was dressed Manhattan-stylish, in head-to-toe black. Her skirt stopped just above her knees, and her sweater was of fine, lightweight cashmere. Her thin belt sported a matte silver buckle. Three strands of varying length silver beads and pearls completed the ensemble.

"How brave to wear such high heels on city streets," I said, smiling my marvel.

She laughed. "I have an event to attend this evening and won't have time to go home and change."

I wore jeans, my favorite ocean-blue cashmere sweater and was sock footed having kicked off my boots. I couldn't help think about all the other shoe choices I'd have made to walk around in by day if I were Dr. S, choosing to bring the Carrie Bradshaw character from *Sex in the City* rock-star heels to slip on just before the event.

"How are you feeling?" she asked after settling into the other wingback chair to my left, pen poised above a lined, white paper tablet. During our first phone session, I had envisioned her taking notes with a giant quill pen in an ornate large book. I gave her the rundown of inflow, outflow, energy levels and sleeping patterns, sitting on the couch with my legs crossed yoga style.

"And how are you *feeling*?" she asked again.

"Ohhh, fine," I said getting the true gist of her question. "Though I'm having some menstrual cramps at the moment." I cringed at "fine." "Fine" and "Okay" are words I help clients retire. I heard my Fairy Tale Fine mask try to hide my continuing anxiety. Dr. S heard it too.

"What is that anxiety about?" she asked.

"I'm afraid all the good stuff I've been doing for my body, like creating balance, is going to dissolve when I get to Texas and then New Orleans for my brother's wedding. I'll be with family for two weeks, and I know how easy it is to fall into old patterns."

Her eyes said, "Continue."

"My Mom's birthday is on Mother's Day this year. I fly in on Thursday night, am hosting a lunch for her on Friday; my brother

235

and his fiancé will come to Texas to be with us for her birthday weekend; then I'll work with clients for three days, get in the car and drive to New Orleans for my brother's wedding weekend, capped off by a birthday brunch for our mom on Sunday that he and I are hosting with all the family in New Orleans." I didn't draw breath as I blurted the long run-on Faulkner-like sentence. I was very much looking forward to being with my extended family, but I was also a little apprehensive.

"Scott is coming to New Orleans for the wedding. He'll meet the, well, the occasional circus that is my family." I paused to consider why I was nervous. "Scott is a teetotaler, and always has been. I don't want him to be too uncomfortable in New Orleans, not only surrounded by my family who definitely imbibes, but an entire city of people who drink."

"Certainly, this won't be the first time he is around people who drink?" she half asked, half stated. I started laughing and shook my head no.

As it turned out, I needn't have worried. Scott loved Bourbon Street, Pat O'Brien's, Café du Monde and all the amazing fresh seafood. He also loved my family. And they loved him. One of my cousins pulled us aside after the last event of the wedding weekend and said, "I am so glad to meet you Scott, and I look forward to the next time we get to visit!" My cousins on my father's side of the family are a good deal older than me as their mothers were nineteen and twenty-one when my father came along, surprising everyone. My grandmother had suffered multiple miscarriages after my aunts were born. She was forty-three when she birthed my father in 1933. Yes, I was also counting on that piece of family her-story.

After my laugh waned, she said, "There's an and there."

I took a moment to consider. "I'm an overachiever for all the people in my life. Despite all my valiant efforts in self-care, I am not very good at it when I feel like others need something from me." I could hear how hard I was being on myself. The Chief Operating Officer of Control and Overachiever masks were on display, big time.

"I know it's an oxymoron because I do care for my body by not ingesting the ever-growing list of what it can't process. I don't eat wheat, cheese, yeast, vinegar, sugar, or sip grain alcohol or wine. I run on the beach. I do yoga. I buy all types of DVD's devoted to core strength, weight training and cardio blasts," I said feeling defensive. I also sounded a tad whiny, full of uncertainty and completely detached from the litany. If I'd been coaching someone saying what I was saying, and how I was saying it, I'd have intruded by calling out the detachment, and then ask what was happening underneath.

Dr. S did that very thing as she gently reminded me that the naturopathic model is one of creating an environment in my body for health, calm, fertility, pH balance, and even love.

"How can you create and maintain a sense of calm and self-care during the next weeks of travel?" she asked.

"I don't know," I said, knowing I did. "I'm afraid between all the fun events and the tight time frame around them and how much I love all the Tex-Mex and Gulf Seafood I'll wind up spilling out of my bridesmaid's dress."

We both laughed, neither of us able to really imagine that reality. I knew I was losing weight in Toronto, as I often do, when traveling for work. One of the "backwards" things about me is that I lose weight dining out repetitively whereas most others gain weight. I think it comes down to the fact that working from a home office most of the time provides way too many opportunities to graze all day in between meals, and there just isn't time or space for that while traveling, especially for work.

The doctor's recommendation was continue feeding my soul with meditation and visualization; continue feeding my body with the pH balancing Zesty Green Soup and anti-inflammatory protein shakes. Thank goodness I was staying with a colleague in Toronto rather than a hotel and had the use of her kitchen.

Dr. S veered the conversation to sustaining my body with more supplements, the naturopathic doctor's prescription. I listened carefully, scribbling notes, as she introduced the new items: a woman's hormone support herbal mix, a glandular support, which had the word "adapt" in the title and some coral powder to mix into the protein shake. Though during my Akashic Records reading, Barb had said the key for me was to balance my hormones, each time Dr. S mentioned the woman's support herbal mix, I got emotional. I'm talking about tears running down my cheeks emotional . . . the kind of tears that you know you can't stop because you aren't in control of where they are coming from.

"Let's muscle test these hormone support formulas," Dr. S said in her gentle way.

I fell in love with the art and science of kinesiology during my first muscle testing experience. I was asked to hold my arm out in front of me at shoulder height and resist the pressure of the teacher pushing down on my arm as I said, "My name is Cat."

My arm didn't budge as it was pushed against. I was then asked to say "Jim," another workshop participant's name. I lost all strength and my arm had no resistance. I couldn't believe how clear my body was and how much my strength diminished when I said, "I am Jim." I use muscle testing on myself daily to see if something is right for me. My body leans forward if the answer is yes and it moves backwards, away from the thing, if it is no.

I was still teary-eyed when Dr. S started to muscle test me. I thought, how on earth am I supposed to stand here holding my arm out and be strong when I want to curl up in a fetal position when she brings those supplements toward me? The first formula she tested received a mild yes in that I did not go completely weak.

"Menopause Support?" I shrieked, reading the label, feeling like a life sentence had been handed to me. I didn't even try to stop the tears. This was not what I had in mind when I heard Barb's words about balancing my hormones being the key.

The next formula tested, my arm went down like a broken tent pole and was a clear no. We moved to the third formula. It was a general herbal support for women's reproductive health and was a slightly stronger yes than the formula for menopause. "Oh, thank God," I said.

In the moment, I decided to chalk up my weepiness to the fact that I was on the emotional roller coaster the second day of my cycle usually brought. I hoped that hormonal balancer might be the thing the Akashic Records were pointing me toward to help me stay fertile. And that hope silenced my curiosity and unease about the huge emotional reaction I was experiencing to the herbal formulas in general. Hadn't I trusted the alternative

MD all those years ago, in spite of my westernized brain's logical doubt, and hadn't his treatment plan been successful? As I was to later find out, there was a hefty price to pay for not listening to what my tears were trying to tell me.

In my typical gung-ho fashion, I immediately added the new supplements to my regimen. In less than three days I was spinning out in hot-flash city, complete with pre-hot-flash-heart-palpitation-mini-anxiety attacks. Only I didn't know I was having hot flashes. At first, I thought the hot flashes were fever spikes and that I was getting sick. It took two weeks and dozens of extra showers before I put it all together. The herbal formula seemed to be causing a huge *imbalance*, despite the fact that it was supposed to create balance. I called Dr. S who was clearly shocked and said to stop taking it. I did, though the hot flashes continued, and I didn't get another period for four months.

I began to think how devastatingly disappointing and ironic it was that although the bulk of my in-person conversation with Dr. S revolved around self-care, I had committed the ultimate act of self-abandonment. Why hadn't I listened to my emotions? I do not normally burst into tears when someone suggests a supplement. I usually do my own muscle testing to see if my body moves forward or backward. Or I'll simply say yes if it feels right and no if it doesn't. My second safeguard failed, too. I usually have trouble swallowing pills that are not right for my body, but I hadn't gagged. I suppose after the initial "crisis" of the growth had been averted, I'd started to slide a little, to become more careless about listening to my inner wisdom. The truth is even with people we trust, we need to pay attention to what's going on inside. I had trusted Dr. K, after all, but I still knew I needed to follow my own instincts on how to heal. In examining this behavior, I saw that by the time I got to Toronto, I had allowed myself to slip into a perspective of mystique around Dr. S. It was like I'd fallen under a spell I don't think she meant to cast, and I didn't know I was in. I had to acknowledge that I was looking for someone to "save" me like the alternative doctor had saved me from a total body invasion of Candida. Yep, I had stopped listening as intently to myself, and by the time I saw her in Toronto, I had handed my power to Dr. S. I missed the opportunity to take charge of my body and life at a crucial moment by failing to listen to my emotions and the wise one within who knows what is best.

My priestess tendency is to move toward a holistic line of thinking and equanimity. And so I wondered, would I have wound up in a slide into menopause at that specific time anyway; if I'd broken the spell and taken that all-important moment of taking control of my life by way of my body? I'll never know.

CHAPTER 28

"Small and Tucked Away"

On my drive into L.A., I noticed how brown and dry the hillsides looked under the hot mid-summer sun. Such a far cry from the lush green hillsides dotted with early spring wildflowers when my healing journey began five months earlier. It had been two months since my last appointment with Dr. K. Still hot-flashing like crazy (accompanied by mini-anxiety attacks) and a missing period (no, not pregnant) had me jumpier than a long-tailed cat in a room full of rocking chairs. During the pep-chat with my mom on the drive, she reminded me that many people were sending good vibes my way, but even that knowledge didn't soothe me.

Before getting out of the car I conjured the image of a sturdy hammock made from big ship ropes. I envisioned lounging in this good-vibe hammock tied to giant, wise, comforting trees that provided me with insights as well as cool shade. In a flash, I saw the hammock was lovingly tied to the trees by my grandfather's large, deliberate, and sturdy hands, just like he'd tied the thick swing rope around the giant tree's branch stretched over my grandparent's patio. "Yes, this is a safe place to rest," I said aloud before opening my eyes.

I settled into Dr. K's waiting room sofa with a deep sigh. Earth, Wind & Fire crooned from the mini-boom-box in the corner to my left. I was reminded of nature's rhythm once more—the Earth's, the Moon's, humanity's, and mine. Are we all so different, I wondered? I remembered just how disconnected from my natural rhythms I felt in the months prior to hearing "surgery," and acknowledged this journey with my ovaries was a big mirror.

Perhaps forgetting to look—and then remembering to look —in the mirror is part of the rhythm. "That's the way of the world," Earth Wine & Fire intoned—yes, I agree. "Higher and higher," they continued. All of a sudden, this song felt like a message from on High.

It's like the mama hummingbird sitting on her nest in the potted tree outside my neighbor Joya's kitchen window. I've hustled by that tree every day, up and down the stairs, coming and going. Joya stopped me one afternoon, whispered, "Look!" and pointed to the nest. I became rooted to the spot, awe-struck. This nest is in Joya's tree. According to the *Medicine Cards* deck, Hummingbird's message is Joy. And Freedom. Baby hummingbirds soon to hatch, spreading more Joy and Freedom. A nest of Joy and Freedom!

Joy and Freedom. Damn fine elements to include in my rhythm. I decided to focus on these as I waited for my name to be called.

"Mary?" The gal from two months ago, once again, did not make a note or remember that I go by Cat. She ushered me into the exam room without the usual blood pressure and weight fanfare. You know you have been to the doctor too darn fre-quently when the BP/weight ritual is waived. I expertly draped the baby-blue paper sheet over my middle and legs as I lay back on the exam table. I turned off the pulsing fluorescent overhead light, and patted the top of the ultrasound screen, as if it were a dog's head. I wanted it to be a good dog today.

Entering the ritual of the same visualization during the first follow-up, I thought this is how talismans become lucky and traditions ensue. I experienced a visceral understanding of a dugout full of professional baseball players wearing their caps inside out, calling them "rally caps" for luck.

"Mood lighting?" Dr. K joked as she entered the exam room, noting the lack of the overhead light, again. Dr. K is a runner too, and we chatted about the merits of track or sand versus concrete. If she hadn't been busy putting a condom on the ultrasound wand and lubing it with warm gel, we might have been chitchatting at a social event. I vaguely noted the absurdity of this; an absurdity equal to a dentist asking you a question while their hands fill your mouth like a giant bite of sushi.

I watched for the furrowed brow and saw a squint instead. That's good I thought—there is nothing large to see so she is squinting! I could feel the probe going back and forth, rotating, moving parts around to see other parts.

"Have you had breakfast?" she asked.

Feeling like a scolded child who refused to eat breakfast, I said, "Umm, no, not yet. Why?"

"Your bowels are moving like crazy." Before I could ask her why bowels would move like crazy from lack of breakfast, she continued on.

245

"Okay," she said slowly stretching out the "kay" as she removed the wand from me, de-condomed it and turned on the overhead light. "There's good news . . . and bad news," she said, the words dripping as slowly as molasses in January. She rolled her stool directly in front of me as I expertly removed my feet from the stirrups and sat up. "The good news is there is nothing growing on the outside of your ovaries." She paused and placed her right hand on my left knee before continuing. "The bad news is there isn't any egg action on the inside of them either. They look small and tucked away."

I felt myself float up out of my body. I couldn't, wouldn't, and didn't want to hear it. She took a breath before continuing.

"As your doctor I'm thrilled to say you are healthy and there are no growths. As your friend, knowing what you want, I am so sorry to tell you, there isn't any action inside your ovaries." We sat there intently looking at each other: doctor to patient, friend-to-friend, woman-to-woman, mother to childless wannabe mother. My pain mirrored in her expression, and the glassy tear in one of her eyes.

I could feel the Category 5 hurricane about to unleash inside of me and knew I had to evacuate my brain because I had too much to do that day to suffer breached levees and storm surges. But I was drowning already, afraid to breathe. As if underwater, I heard Dr. K's "small" and "tucked away" as "shriveled" and "shrunken" and couldn't even pretend to be interested in what she was saying about hormone replacement therapy, egg donors or that my uterus looked healthy and could carry an implanted embryo. I sat there motionless, as if in a trance.

I don't know how long I sat there on the exam table, hunched over my baby-blue sheeted knees after Dr. K left the room. I seemed incapable of movement. It felt like everything stopped, right along with my ovaries. I felt as if my brain and body had separated, and I wondered if this is how psychosis and split personalities begin. Visions of me never getting out of bed again made me want to lie down right there, to numb out, to sleep through the pain in this truth by day so as not to have to go into the world without protective skin, just like I day-slept my grief over Daddy's death.

How could I have thought I still had time? Worn out rage hissed venom at Rich and even more at me. New grief clutched my insides and squeezed so hard I couldn't breathe. I began shaking —like the internal vibrating you do when you have a high fever. The vibrations rippled up and down my body from head to toe.

"No. No. No. This is not my reality," I whimpered faintly, slowly rolling my head side to side. "This *cannot* be my reality."

Suddenly, the phrase "snapshot in time" flickered in the Pollyanna part of my brain. I latched onto the thought that what Dr. K saw on the ultrasound machine was just a snapshot in time, just as the ultrasound snapshot in time five months earlier revealed a growth on my right ovary that was now no longer there.

Vibrating yet numb, I could not feel any sensation of clothes gliding across my skin, as I got dressed. I'm not sure if I really looked at my favorite bespectacled gal behind the desk when she said with affection, "This was the final, nothing-there follow-up, right?" Couldn't she have just said, "No more follow-ups, right?"

I sat in my car staring at the school's playground full of laughing kids at play across from my doctor's office building but not able to focus my eyes. After getting Veronica's work and mobile voicemails, as well as Scott's, before dialing another friend's number it became clear I just had to be with myself. The calm, even-keeled in any life storm part of me took over. It had to, in order to let the stricken, howling one rest. Yep, this could be the moment where my psyche cracks I thought; afraid the truth and my anguish would swallow me whole. Driving home, the parched summer earth felt unbearably sad. I longed for the fertile beauty of spring green hillsides.

CHAPTER 29

The Deep End of the Pool

Finding a bathing suit that fits well—as in one that covers what needs to be covered without covering too much—can be challenging. Finding a suit that makes me feel good about being in a bathing suit is almost a miracle, unless I'm bordering on the anorexic look. I'm curvy and have a short waist so to hear, "You look pretty," from the four-year old daughter of my friend James on the way to the pool made me feel like a Hollywood starlet in my retro black halter one piece (from Target)!

The kids were dancing with impatience to get in the pool as my friend and I slathered sunscreen on them. We began the day with a bike ride, then lunch, and now the promised afternoon swim. Only after they'd cannonballed into the pool did I survey the scene, coating my shoulders with the sunscreen leftovers on my hands. Gulp! There I was *sans* sarong or cover-up at Shutters Beach Resort rooftop pool in Santa Monica, surrounded by pumped up, surgically enhanced, overly tan lithe bodies. I looked down at my legs. Even the tint of my sunglasses didn't disguise the fact that my fair skin looked almost day-glow white. "Easy come, easy go," I thought, saying goodbye to the Hollywood starlet moment.

Pep talk time, I silently acknowledge, "Cat, you are brave to bare your skin and, on this rooftop, you represent busy women everywhere who don't have time to sunbathe." I then mentally congratulated myself further for my willingness to even *be* in a bathing suit, un-tanned, only thirty minutes after lunching on a giant California Pizza Kitchen salad and bowl of tortilla chips. I indulged in an itty-bitty bit of superiority bordering on smugness knowing I had no surgical enhancements, fixes or injections of botulism, though I did wonder whether liposuction is *really* all that dangerous.

"Wait a minute, Cat. You are here to visit with your dear friend James (an early college beau who has turned into a lifelong friend) on his annual vacation to SoCal with his two kids. This is not some pool party scene," I said to myself silently. It was a reunion. Truth? The two kids I'm with don't care what my full belly looks like in a bathing suit. They care that I sit on the edge of the pool, legs dangling in the cool water, watching them swim on one breath from one side of the pool to the other. They care that I express glee over their front flips, back flips, side flips and hip-hop handstands in the water. They care that I watch them fly through the air as their dad tosses them up like a beach ball at a concert. "Watch this!" they shout before the next show-off antic. And my friend, well he and I have known each other for so long, we accept each other unconditionally. Besides, we've both experienced all the up and down weight fluctuations that heartache and adult responsibilities can provoke.

When we arrived poolside, a tiny-toothed, sun-tanned, sweet-smiling little girl was in the pool wearing slightly under-inflated water wings and a pink and green print ruffled bottom. She was splashing about with a few older kids, so we assumed she was their little sister. When the older two got out of the pool and water-wing girl was left alone, James asked her whom she belonged to. She didn't understand the question. So, he uttered the universal, "Mama?" and she pointed to one of the fortyish, lithe, teeny-bikinied women working on her tan. "Mama" was face down on her lounger with a towel covering her head. She could no more have seen her child than I could see the Brooklyn Bridge. My friend and I looked at each other, our eyes both huge, he mouthed, "What the hell?"

A seething overtook me. I imagined myself leaping up and grabbing the five gallon Arrowhead water jug from its cooler stand next to the snack bar, marching over to this oblivious mama and emptying the jug over her like a team of football players dumping Gatorade on their coach after a big win. When she sprang up in shock, grabbing her bikini top to her, since it was untied across her back, I'd stop her from standing by firmly planting one foot on her bony shoulder and pressing her down into the soaking wet lounger.

"You must be vying for the worst mother in the world award," I would hiss. "You are ignoring your child who cannot swim, cannot touch the bottom of the pool, does not speak English and is wearing ill fitting, under-inflated water wings. What the hell is wrong with you?" I would remove my foot from her shoulder and ask, "Don't you know how lucky you are to have a child?" as I fell to my knees sobbing in what can only be called the agony of losing something you never had.

"Did you see that?" The voice of James's little girl shouting, as she bobbed up and down in the water with glee, jerked me back into reality. My heroic stand had only been a movie-like imagining, but I could tell from the trembling in my body that the rage I felt was real.

"Yes, sweetie, I did see that! You made it all the way across the pool on one breath! You are an amazing swimmer!"

She could not see my tear-filled eyes behind the blue-mirrored lenses of my wraparound sunglasses. I looked back over at the tanning mom and was thankful that my personal version of the movie *Anger Management* had not really played out. Being arrested was not on my agenda that day. I also knew that while momentarily satisfying, it would have alarmed the other kids, and I'd feel terrible about that. No, my outrage belonged in my journal and in conversations with friends over cocktails.

I walked across the deck to the Arrowhead water cooler and filled a glass. I didn't know whether to be alarmed, amused or sad when I noticed my thighs rubbed a little. "This is new," I thought, quickly followed by, "Time to re-up the running schedule!" Newer still was I didn't immediately head into the land of self-loathing. Accepting myself "as is" felt a little dangerous, like buying an open-box version of the newest electronic device with the "As Is" warning. "As Is" and "No Warranty" might easily slide into five pounds of salty-crunchy bloat. Yet here I was, somewhere between alarmed and amused.

I walked back to continue in my role as ad-hoc Lifeguard to see that James had become the cool dad and all the kids in the pool were now taking turns at being lobbed in the air like a cannonball. Though still on Lifeguard duty, my mind drifted into journaling mode.

What didn't you choose, Cat? Why aren't you one of these women who have, or at least seem to have, what they want, and are so darn casual about having it? Did they settle or are they living the life they always wanted to live?

"You could be in the X-games," I told one kid as he did a crazy combination of handstand-backflip-spin in the water. "Way to go," I told my friend's son after he swam the length of the pool in one breath.

I didn't choose that life, because I know I'm not built to lounge poolside trying to tan my fair freckled skin I journaled in my mind. I'm like the sensible redheaded woman who just arrived wearing a very large-brimmed hat. She rolled a lounge chair under an umbrella and positioned it so she could see every inch of the pool and slathered more sunscreen on her fair-skinned kids' already zinc oxide covered noses. Well trained, their heads stayed still while their lower bodies squirmed and kicked off shoes. She caught me looking at her and she nodded. I felt included somehow, like now there were two of us counting heads above water.

"Okay, that's enough for now," my friend said, exhausted from twenty minutes of tossing kids into the air.

He swam over to me and said, "Hot tub time! Coming?"

I looked at the hot tub under a gazebo and said, "In a minute. I'm enjoying the sun right now."

As soon as he got in the shaded hot tub, choosing to sit so he had full view of the pool, one of the teeny-bikinied mamas joined him. He and I smiled and nodded at each other across the pool deck. I couldn't stop my mind from wandering to when my last cycle was. I did not want to think, admit or accept the truth: Toronto—three months and counting, still no period.

Each time I'd counted the days and weeks and months on the calendar, I indulged in salty crunchy snacks, my numbing agent of choice. They do a great job of keeping me uncomfortably desensitized and distract me from what I don't have and truly crave. At times I seem to stand back and observe my hand enter the bag and come out with a handful of salvation. I put the seemingly blessed bites in the smallest of my maternal grandmother, Grandmommy's, white bowls, with the embossed rose design along the rim. After filling the bowl I methodically close the pouch and return the snacks to the cabinet. Ten minutes later, as if following shampoo directions, I rinse the bowl and "repeat" the process with another sort of salty crunchy snack. I don't refill the bowl with the same type of salty crunchy salvation, as this would violate the only rule in this game: No repeats in one numbing session.

I rock side to side a bit, trying to find a more comfortable position on the concrete and tell myself, again, these extra five pounds must mean my cycle will start any day now. Still wiggling, I feel moistness in my crotch and wonder if the waited for period has begun. Or perhaps it is just so stinking hot by the edge of the pool that I'm sweating? The viscosity decides the question: it's just too damn warm.

During the prior three months, Scott learned to say nothing, though his raised eyebrow or shaking head tells me I ping pong between Attila the Hun and Weeping Willow. While loading a piece of furniture I bought at a garage sale into the back of my car, he just said, "Yes, dear," to my every direction. He and the garage sale guy shared that rolling-eye guy look. I was more than pleased when after they did it my way, they agreed I did indeed know best how to fit something into the back of my SUV. The thing I want to control most is out of my control, so my Chief Operating Officer of Control opts to control everything and everyone else again.

I'm not sure whether to be grateful and thank the goddess of perimenopause that the panic-inducing hot flash meltdowns have eased. It seems each moment I'm not completely consumed with coaching clients and delivering workshops, the question lurks in the back of my mind, is this really the end? No Hollywood finale? And then I dive into another bag of salty crunchy distraction.

Just then, it seems Sugar Daddy has arrived and Mama of tiny-toothed water-winged girl jumps up, ties her top, dons a cover-up and turns her head ever so slightly to miss his kiss on her lips as she takes the fussy baby boy from his arms.

Sugar Daddy is many more than just a few years older than Mama. As toned, in shape and lovely as she is, he is equally the opposite: out of shape and, well, downright unkempt. No, I would never choose that life—a life with someone I didn't want to kiss on the lips. I don't behave differently when my man is around. And I did not choose loneliness, for that is what I see on her face all of a sudden. Though I still judged her "mama" skill set, I felt a kind of sisterly compassion for her. A few of my friends had married someone just to be married. Let's just say, none of them is very happy.

Later, while James's kids were getting out of their wet bathing suits, I asked him, "What does it say about me that I didn't get this, no, let me be clear, *choose* this life?" In that love-you-no-matter-what friend way, he said, "You and Rich got to do some pretty cool things I couldn't," his eyes and head moved in the direction of the kids. "We all just do the best we can," he said with such tenderness my eyes welled with tears. He reached for and squeezed my left hand.

I appreciated deeply his love and kindness in that moment. Plus there was truth in his words. But I knew I was in the big territory of examining all of my choices—past and in the moment. I knew it would be part of my healing. I knew it would be part of my grieving. I knew that freeing myself from the weight of regret was the only way I could move forward into a new kind of hope's light.

CHAPTER 30

Doing Everything Right

From 2006, before Rich and I were unwinding, until November 2011, I followed an unchanging routine. Upon waking each morning, I slowly rolled onto my left side and with my right hand gingerly felt around the top of my nightstand for the Rite Aid store branded digital thermometer. I placed the thermometer under my tongue and lay as still as possible and waited for the thermometer's beeps. Dutifully, I wrote the temperature down in the little spiral notebook with pastel yellow, pink and blue colored birds on its cover, which I housed in my nightstand drawer.

"Sara and I read *Taking Charge of Your Fertility* and voila, kid #2," emailed my friend James when I told him that Rich and I were arguing more and more about my wanting a child *now*. I methodically followed the advice in the book, which is why I took my waking temperature each morning. I also started looking at the color and consistency of my cervical fluid by way of vaginal discharge. (The stuff that looks like egg whites indicates "get-busy" ovulation time.) I dutifully made those suggested notations too.

In my driven desire for a child, and to enhance my waning fertility, I left no stone unturned. I scheduled an appointment with Dr. Matt; a Chinese Herbalist purported to be a fertility guru. Despite the inconvenient location of his office deep in the heart of L.A.'s northwest San Fernando Valley, several forty-something friends of my friends had miraculously become pregnant after taking his herbal concoctions. (Lynne, my hair gal shared an inspiring story of one of her client's miracles with this herbalist, so I knew it wasn't just urban legend.) From my prior experience with Chinese medicine, I expected to stick out my tongue so Dr. Matt could check the color. I expected him to take my pulse. I expected to answer questions about lifestyle and habits.

Dr. Matt was a man of few words. I sat in the chair on one end of the large table that serves as his desk. He asked me to place my right hand palm down on the table as he opened the small boxes and leather rolls that housed tiny vials labeled in Chinese. After adjusting my hand to lay flatter, he proceeded to run through a series of acupoint palpitations. Though extremely ticklish I tried not to laugh or move too much as he alternated tapping his fingers on various parts of my hand, arm, elbow crease, knee, ankle and toes. His tapping was light yet firm. This rhythmic flow halted only long enough for him to scratch a few notes in Chinese characters. I was both fascinated and dubious, torn between my natural curiosity and a surgeon's daughter skepticism.

No banter. No commentary. No explaining the process. Few words. Only directives as to which way to place my hand, put my foot up on the little stool, take my foot off the stool.

After about a half hour of silence he told me I had mold in my lungs. No surprise: I was in New Orleans four weeks after

Hurricane Katrina, sifting through the very moldy contents of my brother's flooded house. I'd also had a roof leak that took my condo HOA forever to fix, so long that I could see mold growing behind the paint on the ceiling. Dr. Matt also said I had mercury poisoning. Well, no surprise, again, I thought. I called my way of eating "pescatarian." Though mostly vegetarian, I ate things that swam, but nothing that walked, crawled or flew.

I took Dr. Matt's herbs dutifully, assured that ridding my body of toxic mold and mercury build-up would support my fertility. Veronica said the herbs looked like dirt, so that became the moniker for them. "Time for my daily dose of dirt!" While I did begin to breathe more easily and feel rested upon waking, my menstrual cycles began to change in their timing, coming every three weeks, then five, then four, then back to three again. (It was easy to see chaos when I tracked it. But it was painful, too, so I stopped reading what I was tracking.)

A year later when I spoke of exhaustion at a Christmas party in front of one of my goddess sisters, she gave me her acupuncturist's card and said, "Go see her. She really helped me." I went to her acupuncturist who looked at my blood work and said, "Honey, you need to eat some meat. Think of it as medicine." The implication was my periods would normalize once I overcame severe iron deficiency. Continued acupuncture was also suggested. So after over thirteen years of being a "pescatarian" I gulped and ate meat. Not chicken or turkey. I went straight to beef and bison cooked medium rare. Tasty thought the Texan in me. I gained stamina, overcame anemia, and continued getting acupuncture treatments, yet my periods did not return to their prior clockwork regularity.

While Scott slowly regained his strength, he had a setback and asked me to be patient, again. During this setback and almost a year after he left, Rich came back to town on business, and made his case of why we should still be together. He stayed at a hotel about fifteen minutes away from what was now my place but had once been ours.

Over the next few weeks Rich and I went to dinner, and though conversations started out lightly about daily events over salad and appetizers, when we inevitably got to us, we wound up pushing entrees around on plates. One night he told me he'd been seeing a therapist after all my years of begging him to, and I wondered if maybe there really was a chance for us. Then I'd talk to Scott, feel him in my heart, and feel cuckoo. When Rich and I walked on the beach, the pull of habit made it hard not to reach for his hand or find mine nestled into his. Sometimes I'd bend down to look at a shell or a piece of sea glass to help me resist the familiar intimacy that tore at me. I hoped for his healing in therapy, as I felt our passion trying to knit together a new chapter. Yet my wiser self knew our prior chapters could not be erased. After he had moved out, I bound my love of him into a little box inside of me. I was doing everything I could to keep the lid closed. He was doing everything he could to pull off that lid.

A few weeks later, Rich told me that out of all the mistakes he'd made in life he was the sorriest about not being able to give me the thing I longed for most when we were together. After his work in therapy, he decided that if I still wanted his baby, he would try to get me pregnant. But he wasn't sure he was up to raising the child.

I couldn't breathe. I felt like I was in one of those spinning barrel rides where the centrifugal force holds you to the wall as the floor drops away. Only the force of fury kept me upright. My heart and old dreams dropped away, again and for the last time as I knew I would never get beyond those devastating words. A part of me would always love him, but I could not put myself through any more hurt. A few days later, I looked him straight in the eyes and lied, "I don't love you," so that he would leave.

Adding to the mix of that crazy summer was Luke, a friend of one of my childhood girlfriends. When he called, I felt his voice was like smooth, thirty-year single malt scotch it was so warm and resonant. I experienced that feeling of, "wow, what just happened?" Our first phone call lasted for two hours. I wondered if I should explore my initial attraction further and decided, why not? He had two children from a prior marriage and was open to more. My friend James said I needed a closer, as in someone who could close *my* deal. A very successful litigating attorney, I knew Luke was a closer. We both wondered what might have happened if we'd met when we were in our twenties. I had a feeling we'd have stayed together. But he lived in Texas and had to stay there for his kids and even though I played with the notion of moving back there, I couldn't envision it.

Besides, math was never my strength, and the relationship geometric triangle was turning me as upside down as the biologic drive was turning me inside out.

Though honoring my values of romance, fun and love, I was trampling my other core values around loyalty, truth and authenticity. My journal pages filled with phrases of me talking to myself: "You're an idiot," and "You're crazy," and "You are going to hit the wall going one hundred miles per hour," and finally, I saw the truth. Though I'd ripped off my Fairytale Fine mask at the end of my relationship with Rich, I'd started wearing it again. Only this time it looked like me frantically chasing a fairytale ending for my dream. I was upping my odds by trying to increase the number of chances. And I had to admit, I was mad at Scott for almost dying and changing our trajectory. Then I examined the hardest truth of all. In trying not to disappoint anyone else, I awoke to how much I'd disappointed myself.

Three years later, one November morning in 2011, a year and change after I heard "shriveled" and "shrunken" I rolled over and began to reach for the thermometer and froze. The futility of all the paces I'd been putting myself through flooded me. It was like the crazy-town thinking was over.

"I'm a high-functioning mess," I said to my alarm clock. "I'm so busy trying to do everything I can to keep my itsy-bitsy-impossible shred of hope alive, I'm ignoring reality."

That morning, I stopped tracking my temperature; the thermometer and little notebook stashed under a royal blue raw silk Estee Lauder cosmetic travel bag in my nightstand drawer. When I removed the travel bag for a trip, I deftly ignored what was under it.

I didn't finish the last batch of Chinese herb "dirt." I dumped it in the trash instead, recycled the bottle and didn't return to the Chinese herbalist.

I chose "Live in your truth," as my 2012 mantra. The truth howled, whistled, and moaned like a tree branch breaking in the wind. Or perhaps it was the sound of the past, present and future colliding in my heart. As is often the case during such times, at first, I didn't know I was crashing and burning. What I did know was that I continued to melt into pools of hot flash sweat every time I thought about anything having to do with my lack of fertility, babies, and cycles.

More truth roared at me three months later when I looked in the mirror and thought, "Who the hell are you?" Two years after the ovarian journey, I was wearing my grief, physically. My pants were about as tight as they could be without splitting a seam. I knew my body was talking to me. It whispered, "You are wearing your grief as weight because you aren't acknowledging it in the light of day."

Grieving a child that was never conceived doesn't have a place in our society. How do you mourn something that never existed? So I kept my grief to myself. I felt crazy for feeling such profound loss. All that visualizing, all that imagining holding my baby, made it all feel so real. I could still feel a "connection" if you will, to a soul on the other side of "the veil" who really wanted to come through me. Which made me feel nuttier still.

In May 2012, I attended a Women's Weekend at Glen Ivy Retreat Center in Corona, CA. Several of my goddess sisters also attended. We'd been to the Day Spa side of Glen Ivy several times (we loved the low entrance fee that included the clay mud bath pool, various hot tubs, swimming pools and beautiful grounds). The retreat was the weekend after Mother's Day.

Driving to Glen Ivy through Friday afternoon traffic, I told Veronica, "I am a participant *only* this weekend. Give me that look if I go into leader-mode." Veronica has this certain cocked-head, raised-eyebrow look that makes you instantly halt whatever you are doing and examine your motives, and laugh out loud at the same time. She gave me that look. "Yes, really," I said. Lately the lucrative training part of my business had been thriving, and I was grateful.

I had also been intentionally pushing hard so as not to have to think too much about my life, and I was tired. I craved to be in the participant-learner-experiencer chair.

At dinner Friday night, our goddess troop blended easily with the other women. Conversations quickly deepened as we opened up and discovered many "six degrees of separation" moments, which often were really only two degrees like the mother and daughter who knew one of Connie's and my college professors. Later that night in our bunkhouse, one woman brought out a game she'd created that contained question cards. You drew a question card and after reading it aloud, shared your answer. The questions ranged from fun and lively to deeply serious. I drew the card that asked: Do you consider yourself a lucky person? I paused and thought about all the "luck" I'd had in winning raffle prizes, scoring great parking spots, fortuitous meetings with people in positions of power, not knowing they were in positions of power, etc. I thought about my mom calling me a lucky girl. And then the real reason why I think I am a lucky person bubbled up. "Yes, I do. I lived through a car train wreck and am here to say those words. Most don't get to say that." There was a chorus of "wows" and nodding heads. To my right, I could feel someone's eyes boring into me. I turned to the woman who was staring at me wide-eyed. "You *are* lucky," she said, tears spilling from her eyes. "My brother and mother were in a car train wreck and both were killed." Time moved in slow motion and everyone seemed to stop breathing. After a moment, the woman and I stood up and hugged each other for a long time, both sobbing. I wept for her anguish and loss, as well as my own amazing good fortune. I told her how sorry I was, and sorry, too, that I had elicited such a painful memory. She was having none of it, saying what a joy it was to hear that someone had lived through such an event. She said something was released in her in that moment. The "game" continued on until everyone had their turn, but I couldn't stop thinking about train wrecks.

CHAPTER 31

Train Wreck

Tucked into the squeaky twin bed at the retreat center that night, trying not to toss and turn so as not to wake Veronica, I let my thoughts drift back to my train wreck. I was finally ready to relive every part of it.

The party that night in late January 1982, like so many during my senior year of high school, was held because my friend's parents were out of town. A handful of us were actually celebrating our successful speech and drama performances at a regional competition earlier that day, while my math and science-oriented friends celebrated their blue ribbons. I readily enjoyed the keg of beer in the backyard and the Jack Daniels bourbon freely poured from half gallon bottles in the kitchen . . . and wound up pretty drunk. So when a friend told me another girl was saying insulting things about me as the drum major of the all-girl drum and bugle corps, I overreacted. A celebratory evening turned into an alcohol-fueled meltdown.

Thomas, a boy I'd just begun dating, walked up at just that moment; saw my emotional state and offered to take me home.

He'd drunk too much as well, but I was eager to leave and didn't care. He opened the door of his late 1970s Pontiac, and I slid onto the wide bench front seat, my left leg under me. I told him I was hungry, and that we had just enough time before my curfew to hit Jack in the Box for greasy, sober-you-up tacos. We drove the short distance to the local franchise on 39th Street, the opposite direction from my house. Everyone else leaving other parties, and the movie theatre nearby seemed to have had the same idea. The drive-thru line was way too long, if I was going to meet curfew. Still in meltdown mode, I told Thomas to just take me home.

Once back on 39th street heading home, he tried to soothe me by telling me everything would be fine. Looking back, I think my emotional state made him nervous. Funny thing was, I couldn't have cared less what the girl said about me personally—I didn't even like her all that much. It was that she had unfairly criticized my leadership of the corps, which was something that really mattered to me. And I couldn't let it go. So Thomas and I weren't paying attention to the road. We were looking at each other. And when I finally turned my head to the front, it was about ten feet away.

"TRAIN," I screamed, hoping that would stop the car.

I came to with my head and neck twisted and resting on the dashboard, my lower body stuck under the dashboard above the cracked windshield, which my head had smashed. I couldn't move. Someone was shouting at me to stay still, that they were going to get me out of there. I shrieked in terror and pain until unconsciousness overtook me, and I came to again hearing screeching metal on metal sounds. The jaws-of-life were employed to release me.

What I didn't know then but would read in the accident report: The train was traveling across the intersection when our car slammed into it. The car spun and the chrome back bumper got caught on the train, which dragged the car with it until the train could stop. The railroad track was on a rise and on that side of the tracks there is a concrete drainage ditch. I was suspended in a v shape, wrapped around the dashboard, dangling head down toward the bottom of the concrete ditch.

Each time I came to, I yowled in pain. I was told that as soon as they could get the door off, I'd be given something to numb the agony. The rescue crew eventually strapped me to a board and hauled me out of the drainage ditch and onto a stretcher. In spite of the pain shot, I was a caged, wounded animal. I growled, hissed and cussed a blue streak each time they touched me or buckled a strap across my throbbing body. Finally, on a proper stretcher and in the ambulance, another EMT took over and asked me who I wanted him to call.

"Dr. Williford," I whispered, eyes barely open to block out the bright overhead lights.

"I'm sorry, but he's not on call tonight."

Grabbing the man's arm I roared, "He's my fucking father. CALL HIM."

Even in my semi-conscious state, I saw the EMT's face startle before closing my eyes again.

"Shit y'all—this is Dr. Williford's *daughter*. Call him."

News travels fast in a small town, even at 12:30 a.m. on a Saturday night. Many of the kids at the party I attended milled about the hospital lobby. Soon friends who had been at other parties and friends of my parents began showing up.

In the ambulance ride to the hospital, Thomas said how sorry he was, pleading for forgiveness. Reaching across to him with my hand I said something like, "It's OK. I'm OK. I love you."

I'm pretty sure I didn't know if I loved him; I did know I was not OK, but I was high on pain killers and accustomed to placating everyone. I wanted to wipe away that sad, worried look on Thomas's face—even if it meant saying things I didn't feel. Even if it meant hiding how much I was hurting from him.

My dad took over as soon as I was wheeled into the ER. As relieved as I was to see my daddy who would make all of this better, I was terrified. Turns out, my right femur was broken and I needed a pin inserted into the bone.

"Call Marty Haig," my father said to the nurse hovering over me, who was sponging off blood and gently removing shards of glass from my face and top of my head. Dr. Haig, who'd tended to my prior childhood joint injuries (sprained ankle, "water" on the knee, broken fingers and such), was called in to do the surgery. "And call Joe Adams to stitch up her face." Dr. Adams was my father's surgical partner, and our families were very close. Dr. Adams had stitched up my brother's face from an accident with a fishhook when he was twelve years old.

"I'll pump her stomach," my dad said to the nurse. Patients always said he was gentle when removing sutures or surgical staples. At home, bandaging up skinned knees or wrapping an ace bandage around a sprained joint, I had experienced his gentleness. He talked me through opening my mouth as wide as I could as he eased the tube down my esophagus. Once when I gagged, he said to keep my eyes on his and to not look at the tube. After the suction began, he asked, "Hell's bells, Cat, how much beer did you drink tonight?" as the yeasty, musty smelling liquid flowed out of me. I cried my answer, as the tube made speech impossible.

As we waited for the full OR team to arrive, the pain meds given to me in the ambulance wore off and I began to moan and curse again. "Knock her out," I heard my dad say. A nurse injected my IV line with some magical pain-relieving elixir, and I blessedly don't remember anything else until waking up hours later in a hospital room, post surgery. I tried to move my right leg but red-hot pain surged through the entire right side of my body. My neck hurt just as badly, and the headache was staggering. Waiting for the injection of Demerol to knock me out again, I looked up at my mom who was holding my hand, trying to hold back her tears.

"I guess it can happen to me," I said. In spite of the enormous pain my body was in, my heart hurt worse. I couldn't stand the look of fear, worry, disappointment and exhaustion on my parent's faces. I'd much rather someone be mad and gripe at me than be disappointed in me.

My mom squeezed my hand and shook her head as the tears flowed.

I knew she didn't want to be right about all the things she cautioned me about—namely, the potential for teenage car accidents. I was forever trying to ease her worry by telling her with bravado and certainty, "You know I'm a good driver! Besides, nothing is going to happen to me!" She always retorted, "The graveyard is full of young people who had the right of way. And don't get me started on you being a good driver. It is the other people I worry about."

The swelling in my leg did not go down like it should have, in particular, my right foot looked like a balloon. Another X-ray done on the mobile unit in my room a few days after the femur surgery revealed a major fracture on the bone above the arch of my right foot. I got a groovy white cast that visiting friends and family could sign. I thought it was totally cool! A few days later, two physical therapists came to help me out of bed so I could try to walk. When my right leg swung off the bed, a stabbing pain exploded in my knee, followed by a loud pop. Turned out, my knee was slightly fractured when it slammed into the dashboard's metal glove box. The weight of the plaster cast, coupled with gravity, turned the fracture into a full-blown break. The heavy plaster cast was cut off and a lighter, so-called "summer" cast was put on to lessen the weight dragging on my knee. (I've broken my foot twice more as an adult and the lightweight "summer" cast is the standard these days.)

One really odd thing about my time in the hospital was the feel of a "party" or get-together because I knew so many of the staff as they were friends of my parents. When Donna wheeled the mobile X-ray into my room and told me why, she tried to buoy my spirits with her corny jokes. When she came back a second time and took the X-ray of my knee, I told her she could come back to visit but that I never wanted to see that darn machine again. Even though I joked around with her and others, I felt completely over-whelmed by the extent of my injuries. I also felt a foreboding sense that life was passing me by.

Mrs. Bowen, my speech and drama teacher stopped by my hospital room for a visit ten days after the accident. I had been cast as Queen Aggravain in the spring musical, *Once Upon a Mattress*. While not much of a singer, broad comedy character singing I can pull off. We'd begun rehearsals two weeks before the accident and

Mrs. Bowen was stopping by to check on my progress. I told her with earnest conviction that I would absolutely be able to do the play—we had three weeks before opening night and I assured her I had all my lines memorized and that I could use crutches by then, or do the role from a wheelchair if need be. The more her eyes looked at me with sympathy, the more I ramped up my pitch. I knew I would be able to do the show and had to convince her.

"I don't think we can have you do the role in a wheelchair—there is a fast costume change and not much room backstage," she said thinking aloud. Then definitively, "Your understudy will do the role. You need to focus on getting better."

My mom's dear friend Fern, who was keeping me company that morning, sat behind Mrs. Bowen. She cried the tears I wouldn't —at least in front of Mrs. Bowen.

After Mrs. Bowen left, the hard news settling into me, I began to sob out words like, "not fair" and "why me?" Fern held my hand and hugged me as best she could hug me in the hospital bed. Later that afternoon, she told my mom about Mrs. Bowen's visit and I heard them both crying for my heartbreak in the hospital hallway, out of my line of sight. Reality set in. I wasn't just going to miss a few weeks of school. I would miss playing the fun ham-it-up role in the musical, I would miss school dances and I would miss out on leading the corps as drum major in spring parades and tryouts for new members.

Lying as still as I could in the hospital bed, waiting for yet another round of drugs to make the pain stop, I remembered the dream I'd had the Friday night before the accident. I was in Thomas's car. We were driving up to the high school, and wham— we were in a car accident. In the dream it was just a fender-bender, no big deal, no injuries. I don't remember if I told Thomas about the dream on the bus coming back from the speech and drama contest, but I do remember telling him I was going to the party with two friends, and that I'd see him there. But somehow, fate or destiny had him witness my emotional meltdown and offer to take me home. It hadn't been planned. It happened because one thing led to another, until it seemed inevitable that I would end up in Thomas's car, at just that moment. So I interpreted the dream to mean the accident was supposed to happen. Even more, that if my leg, foot and knee hadn't broken as a result of getting into a car with an inebriated boy behind the wheel, I would probably have rolled out of bed and broken my leg or knee. The accident seemed predestined.

My mother didn't buy it. "Honey, that is ridiculous. You wouldn't break your leg rolling out of bed—it is only a few feet to the floor." Her practicality was having none of my theory.

"OK—maybe not rolled out of bed but maybe tripped going down the stairs." Her look of incredulity made me double down on believing my new view. This was meant to be.

But I couldn't shake the feeling that I was missing something, even though seatbelts became my new personal law. What was missing, I would later realize, was the cost of overriding my intuition. I had to believe the accident was inevitable, to protect myself from the truth: I hadn't listened to the dream. I hadn't listened because I didn't yet know how to examine my nightly dreams.

I was released from the hospital the Saturday morning of the high school Sweetheart Dance, exactly two weeks after the accident. Because I also missed the next several weeks of school, friends continued to visit me, coming to the house every day with class notes and homework assignments.

My bedroom was on the second floor of the house, and the second week recuperating at home I learned to scoot up and down the stairs on my derriere, since crutches are impossibly dangerous on stairs. When my father came home from the hospital at night, he came up to my room to visit. One evening he asked if I'd done my bed exercises for my knee. "It hurts so bad, Daddy. I didn't do them today."

"Fine—walk with a limp for the rest of your life," he said as he turned on his heel and walked out the door. He intentionally put the fear of limping into my head so I started doing the exercises right then, moaning through them all. He came back in my room when I was done and suggested I do them about an hour after taking the pain medication and they'd hurt less. He was right.

I also had to scoot up and down the stairs on my derriere when I went back to school. The only accessible elevator in the school was an open lift, built for wheelchairs and not standing passengers. I was still on pain killers which had to be administered by the school nurse, and I was shocked at how many students I didn't even know very well approached, asking if they could buy some from me. Even if I'd had them in my purse, the answer would have been no. I still needed them to get through the day and had no intention of becoming a dealer.

When Dr. Haig and the rehab specialist asked me what my goals were, I said, "To walk across the stage at graduation without crutches. And to water ski this summer." They said the first was possible if I continued my rehab exercises, but they agreed my waterskiing days were over. Just watch me, I thought.

Oh, yeah, I water skied that summer. I snow skied the next winter. I also danced to slow songs a little at the late spring senior dances.

Home for spring break, my brother took me to see the car in the local wrecking yard and I promptly threw up. "How did Thomas and I live?" I asked my brother. I could see in his kind eyes he was sorry he'd brought me to see the car. I wasn't. I needed to understand how close I'd come to death and yet survived. I needed to feel lucky again.

Much to my parent's horror and disappointment, I continued to date Thomas, who in their eyes remained the boy who drove me into a train and almost killed me. We dated until the next fall after I'd gone away for school. His injuries were minor comparatively— a few cracked ribs and a badly bruised knee. He made me laugh, and not unlike people who go through a traumatic event together, a deep bond was forged. Nobody else I knew had been in a car accident with a train. Besides, I couldn't stand to abandon him. It might make it look as if I blamed him for what happened.

People naturally assumed Thomas hadn't been paying attention. How else do you miss a train already going across the intersection? And it was true. But I also knew he had been trying to look after me in my hyper-emotional state, telling me the girl who cast the aspersions was wrong, an idiot and all the things we say to people we care about who are hurting from the sting of an insult. He had tried to do the right thing by getting me away from the situation. I also felt partly to blame because if I'd not wanted to go to Jack in the Box in the first place, we'd have missed the train. If we'd waited in the drive-thru line at Jack in the Box, we'd have missed the train.

If I hadn't gotten in the car with him, and instead asked the friends I went to the party with to take me home, Thomas and I would have missed the train. All were my calls. And then there was the dream. What if I had known to listen to my intuition via the dream? What then? But there is this too: we were just stupid acting, inebriated teenagers, who didn't think anything bad would ever happen to us.

Though I met my goals of total recovery and walk without a limp, my right leg is shorter than my left leg when it comes to pant leg hems. I used to set off metal detectors at airports until the femur bone fully encapsulated the break points around the rod. And my right knee is what I call cranky when I run too far or jump off something and land with too much weight on my right leg. The migraine headaches I've been plagued by since early menstrual years ramped up shortly after the accident and the neurologist diagnosed them as cluster headaches. They continue to this day, as does the neck pain. And for a dozen years or so after the wreck, slivers of glass worked their way out of the top of my head.

Lying in bed that night at the retreat, reliving the trauma, I felt the coldness of the rod in my right femur. I let myself mourn losing the role in the musical. I allowed the rage I had never really let myself feel about the seeming unfairness of the circumstances. I felt the helplessness of it all. I also experienced sympathy for Thomas who was teased mercilessly about not seeing the train until it was too late to stop the car. I also understood more deeply my mom and dad's resentment at Thomas for almost killing their little girl. I felt the ache of taking responsibility for things that weren't mine to take responsibility for, all the way back to when my father almost died when I was eight years old. I'd been taking responsibility for my friends, my family, my colleagues, and my boyfriends —not as in to blame for things—rather to fix, rescue, save and relieve.

Why on earth had I assuaged Thomas's immediate guilt by telling him it was OK and that I loved him? But I knew. On that drive in the ambulance to the hospital, and despite how much I hurt, I didn't want to admit I was injured badly. I didn't want to admit life had just taken a wild left turn. I saw that I often collapse over-responsibility, letting people off the hook and forgiveness into each other. Forgiveness is good, over-responsibility and assuaging not so great.

I also felt the guilt of wasting time, waiting for my beloved Rich to catch up to my dream. I thought he was like daddy—he would take care of me, give me everything I wanted, and spoil me. I found myself wishing I'd already known to really listen to and heed the circumstances in my dreams before that accident, because I have to believe I wouldn't have gotten in the car with Thomas. I thought about timing—the timing of the Universe, seasonal timing and shifts, my body's timing and the timing of learning to listen to intuition and wisdom. I thought about the time I did follow my intuition after a spirituality workshop when I stopped for a bottle of water at a 7-11 in Marina del Rey at 10:30 p.m. before my half hour drive back to Burbank. There was a line of people and the tape in the cash register had to be changed. Several times I thought about abandoning my place in line and heading home but *something* in me kept me rooted to that line. Finally home, I parked my car in the underground lot of my apartment building, and had a funny tingle up my spine as I got out of the car. I walked to the elevator and when it opened, I saw blood smeared down one wall.

Just then the manager came into the garage from the street level gate near the elevator with the police. An officer escorted me up to my apartment. The only information I could squeeze out of him was that a woman had been attacked in that elevator about fifteen minutes prior...the length of time of my 7-11 delay.

My memories, emotions and thoughts swirled around me and through me all night, until dawn's light filled the room. I finally dozed off and slept for a few dreamless hours before breakfast.

In the women's retreat formal circle that morning, we were asked the question, "Why are you here this weekend?" I listened to everyone who shared before me, uncomfortable in not having planned an answer in advance. I heard the other women say everything from, "Celebrate my dream come true," from a woman who'd so recently given birth she was nursing and had her baby with her; to "Stop judging myself," from an outwardly successful business woman; and from the mother-daughter duo, "Forgiveness." I began to shake inside while the woman to my right shared she was there to heal her grief over the loss of her beloved husband of forty years. I offered her my hand, and she squeezed it tight. And just like that, when it was my turn to answer the question, I knew what I had to say out loud.

What tumbled out of my mouth felt like somebody else said it, " . . . to release my dream of having a child come through my body." And then haltingly, " . . . I acknowledge my fertility cycles are . . . complete."

I couldn't breathe for a moment, the grief of knowing I was out of time flooding my chest. I immediately wanted to send one of those "retract the message" emails. I'm surprised I didn't clap my hand over my mouth.

And then my shoulders fell, my clinched chest relaxed, and I felt a calm descend through me. For the six months prior, but in many ways, for years, I had built a dam around the truth. Now it was released, and with it a tension I didn't even realize was there that had become so much a part of me.

I looked at the women opposite me in the circle. One was weeping; another had her hand on her heart chakra. One about my age sat with crossed arms over her chest, very much on the defensive. Then I looked at Veronica sitting a few chairs away to my left and tears streamed down her cheeks for me. My other goddess sisters were teary eyed and looking at me with deep love. That's when I recognized the heat of my own tears.

I'd been stoic about it all for so long. Stoic, and yet convinced there was still a possibility, no doubt born from my innate optimism, stubbornness and the skill of hope. I developed the skill of hope as a survival tool during my father's long six months in ICU before his death. In my recognition of why I was at this women's retreat around *Mother's Day*, that fortress dam inside of me collapsed into dust.

I've been a coach for 25-plus years, and I'm about to say something wildly under-spoken in the circles of positivity and vision I run in. *Not every dream comes true, no matter how many times you visualize the reality you desire, or how many smart things you do just right, or how much action you take.* That doesn't mean we shouldn't dream, visualize, or take actions to support our dreams. It just means that sometimes we are simply blind to the consequences of the collection of our prior choices until a dam breaks inside of us.

In my case, the collection of my choices to stay with Rich for seventeen years, hoping we'd find ourselves on the same page around children, and then the choice to wait for Scott to get back on his feet. Often, daily actions of habit fly in the face of vision and dreams. My values of love, loyalty and passion competed with my value of creating a family. I brilliantly honored those values daily in my relationship with Rich, and for Rich. I didn't honor loyalty, though, to my own dream, or allow myself the passion for it. I made his dreams more important. So I lived out my value of family by being very present for my brother and mom during surgeries, hurricanes and life events, but did not generate my own family. Honoring values can be a tricky thing—did I honor them more for others than for me? Yes, I did. Yet as long as somehow a value is lived out, we go along to get along. Until we don't because we can't. And we can't because once conscious of the chasm between our dream, our choices, and behavior, we can no longer soldier on.

My profound, out loud and very public release of my dream during the Women's Weekend came during the last day of May's waning moon cycle. (The waning moon begins one week after a full moon and is considered an optimal time for release and completion.)

The burden of my secret grief was further released while walking the herb garden labyrinth later that afternoon—it had been six months since my last cycle. I walked into the center of the labyrinth full of the intention to release my dream of becoming a mother. I knew it was time to acknowledge the transition from the Maiden/Mother archetype and embrace the archetype I was evolving into: the Matriarch/Mentor. My slow pace reflected a continual prayer for inner peace, surrender, and truth. At the center of the labyrinth I asked my beloved Future Self and wise one within, JoyFulllLight, to join me. I felt her energy by way of tingles on my arms, legs and neck. She spoke before I could ask my question: "You know the way forward." I wasn't sure at all that I did; yet I decided to trust her words as I had so many times before. "As you walk out of the labyrinth, don't think. No more blame. No more shame. Simply experience this moment. Smell the herbs, feel the sun on your skin and focus on your breath." I followed her directive and emerged from the labyrinth without letting my inner judge beat the crap out of me emotionally for all the ways I betrayed my own dream. I turned around and said aloud, "Labyrinth," knowing I'd just found my new perspective. "Taking responsibility is different than continual blame and shame."

Back home I did what I do best—hurled myself into busyness, too damn raw to engage in deep reflection. I needed a scab to form, to let the slow-flow-lava-like grief heal. When I caught myself picking at the freshly formed scab with self-recrimination for waiting too long to say "Now," to Rich *and* Scott, I invoked my new perspective by saying aloud, "Labyrinth," and just like that my energy shifted and possibilities for acceptance opened up.

Weeks later during a morning meditation, a familiar self-recrimination crept in and jolted me out of the peacefulness. "Labyrinth!" I shrieked, standing up in the middle of my living room and, like Scarlett O'Hara, shaking my fist at the heavens. "No more left-over boxes filled with remnants of grief, anger or sadness. And no more blame."

That's when I knew I had to experience a ceremony with my sisters in order to bring completion to my release. I immediately wrote the "Circle Up" email, knowing the sheer act of sending it would set in motion more healing, releasing and cleansing of the still festering wound beneath that fragile scab.

TRAIN WRECK

Dear Ones,

Last month at the retreat at Glen Ivy, I uttered some words out loud for the first time. I think they've been trying to tumble out of me for a while now and I've held them in, not wanting them to be true.

When asked why we were attending the Women's Weekend, I listened to everyone who shared before me, not knowing my true reply until it was my turn to speak.

I said something like, "... I acknowledge my fertility cycles are ... complete."

I ask you to gather with me in ceremony to mark this big truth.

I've been thinking about the power of intentional completion and release. As a coach, I support my clients with this all the time. Let's support each other Sunday evening to release that unspoken, unacknowledged thing lingering in our lives.

To prepare: Identify one thing it is time to call complete—either in fact or by its emotional hold on you. It may be an old dream or desire, painful experience, circumstance, physical pain – or you can join me in bidding adieu to regular, fertile monthly cycles.

Grandmother Moon is waning which means she will help us with our releasing.

Love, Cat

CHAPTER 32

Put a Fork in It

Dear Ones,

You may want to bring items for the altar that signify what you want to release, in order to "de-charge" or neutralize them. Example: I'm bringing fertility books, the thermometer I took my temperature with every morning, the notebook I tracked my waking temperature in, etc.

I sent this addendum email to my "Circle Up" goddess sisters the evening before our Sunday gathering. The idea had been inspired earlier that day after I'd done a bit of "pick and put" (my goddess-sister and professional organizer Tamara's shorthand for pick things up and put them away). I slid my hand under the Estee Lauder royal blue travel bag and my fingers found the Rite Aid digital thermometer housed in its clear plastic case. Then I fingered my way to the very back of the drawer for the little 4 x 6" spiral notebook and pulled it out. Already leaning over, left hand on top of the mattress, I simultaneously grew dizzy, weak, and nauseous. I knelt on one knee so I wouldn't fall over.

The otherworldly sounds coming from my mouth sounded like the rumble the earth makes just before an earthquake.

"No, please, don't start, don't do this now—let it out in ceremony tomorrow," I pleaded to the goddess of emotion inside me.

My stomach seized, tears and wails spewing out with a volcanic force. How could two innocent little items tucked away in a nightstand drawer elicit this response? "Buried, not tucked away," I shrieked, unconcerned that my windows and sliding glass doors were wide open for all the neighbors to hear me.

Rolling off my knees I sat on the floor, knees tucked under my chin, nestling into the L-shaped "corner" that the side of the bed and nightstand made. I craved protection but I felt naked and on display to myself.

I thumbed through the little spiral notebook, stunned by all the filled pages. I couldn't read any specific entry, my tears acting like cataracts. But I knew those pages, which tracked my temperature and cervical fluid, held my optimism, discipline and my now interred dream.

"Please stop, please wait till tomorrow, *please* stop," I pleaded, knowing the migraine effect on my body from huge emotional storms. The emotional goddess within assured me that she would only be appeased by full throttle release.

Like clockwork, I felt my low back go out, starting the chain reaction that would send me to the chiropractor. Next, my neck seized into a jillion knots, as if I were reliving the train wreck, cracking through the windshield all over again. I tried to engage my breath as a means of halting my body's breakdown, to no avail.

"Maybe if you stop crying now, you can avert a migraine," I advised myself blowing my nose again. But I knew it was too late.

One advantage of knowing how my body talks to me (when I listen) is being able to stop doing something that is going to trigger pain or physical injury. By paying attention, I learned which foods trigger migraine. I also know the signs of a migraine that can't be stopped. This was one of those times.

Clutching the thermometer and spiral notebook, I got up and placed the handful of used Kleenex into the trashcan. I walked unsteadily to the kitchen and placed my two fertility trackers in the canvas bag from Avenue Beauty, my head beginning to rage.

I opened my "snack" cabinet and glowered at the empty shelves. I thought about going to the store and getting the party-size bag of tortilla chips. I opened the refrigerator and the kale, chard, celery, cucumbers and spinach sang a promise, "Juice me and you will feel better."

So, instead of kowtowing to the much younger me and pulling out the tequila to make a batch of my semi-famous margaritas, I made a green juice. Besides, alcohol is kerosene to a migraine's fire. I sipped the juice slowly, enjoying the enzyme high almost as much as the first flush of a giddy-making margarita. With pure vitamins and chlorophyll surging through my blood, and feeling less shaky, I decided to continue my quest to collect the rest of the fertility paraphernalia. Steamrolling through a migraine was nothing new for me. And sometimes, by losing myself in action, or concentrating on a specific task, I redirect my attention away from the physical pain.

I walked into my office and sat cross-legged on the floor in front of the wide and deep bookcase that had been Rich's. The fertility books stood next to each other on the bottom shelf. One by one, I placed them gently in my lap, my hands covering the title of the book on top of the stack. I wanted to protect my heart from seeing the title and the hope it had once offered.

"This is just a book, Cat. A book. Information. That's all," I said aloud, knowing I had to dispel its hold on me.

I picked up the top book and flipped through to see how many pages were dog-eared. I didn't dare linger on any highlighted phrases but I knew what the pages said. In one swift lurch my juice high was gone; I was sobbing uncontrollably again. I tried to comfort myself by curling into a fetal position around the books in front of the bookcase, resting my head on my right arm.

My back, neck and head were so far gone with pain I didn't pretend I could stop the tears. When my right shoulder blade popped out of joint, I knew the physical manifestation of the emotional storm was complete. Well, not complete as in over, but at least I wasn't waiting for my spinal column to go further out of alignment. I was like a jack-knifed transport truck dumping my emotions as cargo strewn across an interstate highway.

Finding no comfort physical or otherwise in my fetal curl, I sat up, gathered the books into my lap again, wrapped my arms around my torso and rocked myself very tenderly from side to side. My howling sobs slowed to a gentle, steady stream. When that stream ran dry I returned to the kitchen and put the fertility books in the Avenue Beauty bag. "Another half box of Kleenex down," I said to the books. My sinuses were so inflamed it felt like my head might just split open from the pressure. I knew an over-the-counter pain reliever wasn't going to make a dent in the pain, so I didn't bother.

Instead I slathered Icy Hot all over my neck and lower back. I heated my sage-green sinus pillow in the microwave and got into bed. Draping the warm, lavender scented pillow over my eyes shutting out the late afternoon sun and relaxing my forehead muscles, I silently began a Reiki healing on myself and blessedly fell asleep. When I woke, the room was dark and the pounding in my head had diminished enough to sit upright.

Driven by some supernatural force to complete my mission, I went back to the kitchen and gathered the prenatal vitamins I'd stopped taking months before and placed them in the bag.

Next, I went to my desk, opened the top drawer and pulled out my old health insurance card: the card that represented maternity insurance. After agonizing about letting go of the exorbitantly expensive insurance coverage that included maternity, I found out that my new policy, at less than half the price, included maternity. In fact, on the new policy I could be a man and have maternity coverage. I placed the old card in the bag along with everything else.

I got in the shower and communed with Kuan Yin, the goddess of women's self-love and self-healing, just as I had that morning two years prior, after hearing, "First, I'll baggie the ovary and growth to contain any rupture."

I lifted my face to receive Kuan Yin's blessing by way of warm water. I turned my throbbing right temple into the shower stream for her to bless. I rotated my head so my left eye received her powerful flood of warm water. I turned around and asked her warmth to melt the jillion kinks in my neck. I repeated this rotation three more times, breathing in Kuan Yin's love, the steam and experiencing something like acceptance.

"Kuan Yin, I don't know what's next. I don't know anything right now. Except that I'm tired. I'm so very tired of feeling ashamed and like a failure," I said, beginning to cry again.

"Darling, you are no failure and there is no need for shame. You simply made choices. You are no less a woman, goddess, or priestess. This was your path," said Kuan Yin. I thought about all the years I wore the self-imposed mantle of failure following daddy's death six months after my kidney was placed inside of him. I had finally shaken off that mantel when I realized I— someone who'd never taken a business course in college—had created a coaching business at a time when practically no one knew about coaching.

Later that night, sitting on the soft sofa in my dimly lit living room wrapped in my enormous white terry-cloth spa-like robe, I remembered the phrase, "I'm raising women." Fifteen years earlier, when I was in my early thirties, a client had sent me a handwritten card with these words, "Thank you from the bottom of my heart for raising me, for giving me access to the love and support my mama couldn't give me as a child. I now know how to love." That same year, a woman in her forties encouraged me to 'get busy' in the baby-making department. I said, "I'm too busy raising women. Women who didn't get the love and support they needed in childhood. Somehow, my life purpose of, 'Know the Light of Love is Inside. Share it,' involves the nurturing of women through love, compassion and natural positivity."

"Yes. I am complete with my cycles. I am ready to release the dream of giving birth," I whispered.

I felt my Chief Operating Officer of Control mask slip from me, weary from all her striving. She looked like a flat paper doll a child had left in the corner in favor of some new shiny, pretty toy.

CHAPTER 33

Release and Goodbye

We gathered for our Release ceremony at Veronica's home, placing our objects on the altar. Several of my sisters who had always thought they would have children and didn't, were also there to release their version of that dream. I unpacked my bag of books, vitamins, thermometer and tracking notebook. Also adorning the altar were one sister's generational family Christening gown, hand tatted booties, and a silver rattle. An unmarried sister brought her "Hope Chest" and another sister laid upon the altar her first marriage's wedding rings.

Emotions raw and exposed, our tears flowed as we grieved out loud. We grieved our loss of fertility; we grieved what never was; we grieved the relationships we left in order to pursue our dream of children; we grieved the relationships we left in order to pursue our dream of career; we grieved our broken heartedness. We grieved and released, and in the process, we grew stronger and more resilient.

Our sisters who had chosen early in life to refrain from having children witnessed our pain and release with loving eyes and words of empathy. Our sisters who had children and grandchildren held us tenderly. We all shared what dreams we were there to release. Some grieved lost years to too much work. Others grieved feeling inept at times as mothers. We grieved together as friends, sisters and modern women living in a complex world where each decision has intended and unintended consequences. We each found new layers of self-forgiveness as we saw ourselves mirrored in our adored sisters. If we wouldn't judge, chastise or loathe our sisters, why would we do those things to ourselves? We released our individual and collective pain to the waning moon and each other.

In any ceremony of release, it is wise to make space to claim the new. Even if you don't know the next dream, the invitation is to claim what you want to experience. So I claimed and stood for inner peace. I stood for experiencing my creative energy through writing, art and music, and most importantly, I stood for love. I claimed and stood in my fresh stage of life and archetypal energy, that of the Matriarch. (I had released the Maiden and Mother archetypes, and I knew the Crone was still far into the future. Actively engaged in life, yet no longer "mothering" people, the Matriarch is free to create, contribute and mentor without constraints of daily, active nurturing responsibilities of young ones at home. She is today's middle-age woman—vibrant, healthy, strong, intent on making a difference in the world with her wisdom.)

Not long after the ceremony, I realized along with releasing my dream, I had to release Scott. When I still clung to my dream of children and our life together as a family, I denied (or had chosen to ignore, more like it) the fact that he was still caught up in rebuilding himself, his body and his life. And that he would continue to be so for the foreseeable future, precluding actually moving forward in life as a partner.

One Sunday morning, after an OK but rather boring weekend together, I woke knowing that this was the day to end the comfortable, friendly loop we had evolved into. I knew I couldn't let him leave without speaking my truth. We sat on the sofa after breakfast, I took a deep breath and said quietly, "This isn't working. It isn't enough for me. I need passion, romance and commitment. I'm not trying to shame or blame or guilt you into anything . . ."

He held up his left hand like a white flag. I stopped talking. "I know. You deserve so much more than I can offer. I'm more than sorry," he said with profound sadness and a tinge of relief. We sat in silence. As a wave of grief washed through us, we'd squeeze the other's hand.

Once I had done the really hard work of releasing my dream of bearing a child, it became easier to see with clarity the other dreams, relationships and wants that were worthy of release.

Releasing and healing myself in the big stuff, allowed true alignment. I stopped fighting and controlling. I stopped trying so hard to make us into something we were no longer going to be.

That Sunday, Scott and I lovingly released the dream that began before his insides exploded and before my fertility ran out. I walked with him to his car, and we stood locked into an embrace for several minutes. I felt his tears on my cheek. "Life," he said before breaking the hug.

Indeed.

We remain close friends to this day.

CHAPTER 34

Baby Dolls

I don't really remember the Christmas I received my first Madam Alexander baby doll, but I do remember carrying her around with me everywhere. I don't mean dragging her by the hair like many a little girl does. I mean carrying her on my hip like my mom carried me. I *loved* my little Pussy Cat baby doll!

Every few years I received a new baby doll for Christmas, each one a little larger than the last one. I played dress up with them using my old baby clothes. I put them in sleeper pajamas at bedtime and "changed" their diapers just as my mom taught me to. (Yep, cloth diapers with those safety pins with little ducks on the closure!) I would cradle them in one arm and rest an old glass baby bottle to their pouty little mouths. When I imagined the right amount of time had gone by for feeding them, I'd hold them upright on my chest and "burp" them with a little cloth over my shoulder, swaying slowly from side to side.

My mom gave me the bassinet that was originally my uncle's and that my brother had slept in, to play with and warehouse my sleeping dolls. I put the bassinet under my bedroom window on a little table and treated it like a crib. While I was at school, the dolls sat on my bed, waiting for me to come home and play with them. My mom studied fashion design in college, and not only did she make many of my clothes, she made clothes for my dolls, too.

My love of dolls apparent, just about everyone in my family at one time or other gave me a Madam Alexander storybook doll or Barbie for gift-giving occasions. Pretty soon I had all the doll characters from *Little Women* and each time my parents traveled, they brought me a doll representing the local culture.

I played with my baby and Barbie dolls until I was in my early teens. Then my love of theater and acting consumed me, and I rehearsed for plays or speech and drama contests after school.

Sometime during early junior high school, the Barbie's got put in their cases and up on the shelf on the right side of my closet. The storybook dolls got taken off the open shelves and placed in a new display glass cabinet to protect them from dust. The bassinet of baby dolls got put up on the left closet shelf, where they stayed until the little table under the window was replaced by an antique settee from my grandmother's house. I put the dolls back into their original clothes and lined them up on the settee. As an adult, I loved seeing them there when I returned for a visit. Every once in a while, I'd pick up the biggest one, the large Pussy Cat, and place her on my hip or hold her to my chest in an embrace.

For years, those baby dolls hung out on the settee. For twenty-five years, in fact, until Hurricane Harvey flooded the downstairs of my mom's home. That first week my brother and I were there after the waters receded was chaos. Friends furiously packed up items above the flood line and we brought the boxes upstairs or to a storage unit. With the downstairs being handled, I turned my attention to the upstairs rooms. When I walked into my room, I saw my baby dolls staring intently at me from their perch on the settee, as if to say, "Help us!" I looked to my right and the story-book dolls in the cabinet seemed to be asking me to help them too. "Please get us out of here! It is so hot and humid."

I taped up some big moving boxes and began swaddling my baby dolls in tissue paper rather than the baby blankets I used to wrap them in. I gently laid the biggest Pussy Cat into the box and her little cry box let out what sounded like a scared bleat. I began crying, too, as I enfolded the smaller Pussy Cat and Puddin' dolls in tissue paper, and then the dozens of storybook dolls. I took two boxes of carefully bundled and carefully stacked dolls to the climate-controlled storage unit.

How did I get here, I wondered? How on earth did I get here? Me—someone whom so adored my baby dolls and playing "mama" —how did I become a middle-aged woman with no children?

Yet here it was staring me in the face. Why had my mother and I kept all the baby dolls just so, and protected the others from dust all those years? For my dear baby girl, of course. We kept them all for my little girl to play with at Grandma's house. We kept them all for an imagined and expected little girl and granddaughter that was not to be in this lifetime.

As much as Hurricane Harvey's floodwaters completely altered my mother's reality, those same waters had me once again confronting the very big sadness and grief about what I never had. And I again had questions—lots and lots of questions about choices in life rolled around in my head and my journal. I suppose the silver lining is in how gentle I've been with myself when I reflect and exhume the ghosts of longings past. I have stayed away from the self-recrimination I indulged in years ago. I have allowed the tears to flow without judgment. I have loved myself through it all. And I have tried to live my father's instruction to me—receive love.

Here is what I've learned: I made a series of choices based on love and doing my best that honestly, I'm not sure I'd make differently if I were offered the chance for a do-over.

When I've mentioned this doll experience to other women my age, particularly the ones who find themselves mid-life without kids or a partner, well, let's just say they get it—the feeling of saving things for that one magical day that never materialized.

Recently, my cousin Mandy was in southern California visiting her daughter at a local college and had dinner with my mom and me at a sweet little café. For some reason we were talking about Hurricane Harvey, and some of the blog posts I wrote about my experiences. I told her I'd included in this book, my day of swaddling dolls in acid free tissue paper. Sitting next to me in the booth, Mandy turned to look at me and started to laugh, though trying not to, "It doesn't always go like you think, Cat."

"What do you mean, I asked?" puzzled by her non sequitur.

"Well, when I ceremoniously presented one of my Madam Alexander baby dolls to Sadie (her daughter), she shrieked and ran away, terrified, as if I'd just presented her with an evil *Bride of Chucky* doll!" She held my hand under the table as all three of us laughed until our eyes were moist with acceptance. Mom said, with all her wisdom from beautiful and painful experiences, "No, it doesn't always go like you think it will. But life keeps going and we go with it."

JoyFullLight whispered to me the night the goddesses gathered with me as I released my dream of giving birth, "New dreams are born out of the funeral pyres of old dreams. New life force energy is released when the burden of grief and shame is lightened. New worlds open when old worlds whither. No, it didn't turn out quite as you thought it would. I assure you, though, we have plenty of adventures to come!"

She was right. My seasons of Maiden and Mother have given way to my season of Matriarch. In this new stage, I experience a different kind of fertility in my creativity that extends to completing this book. In this new stage, I am unapologetic about who I am. I no longer chase a dream past its prime. Instead, I focus on loving fully, others and myself. Oh, yeah, I also focus on receiving the love offered by those in my life! It feels good and it feels right, which is different than trying to do everything right.

Oh, the learning. Oh, the healing. Here's to the adventures to come. Blessed Be!

Acknowledgments

Making public my gratitude in the Acknowledgments pages may be my favorite part of writing this book. After I'd written the first draft of this section, I experienced the blessing of support from such rich circles of love, care and connection. You are each like unique and natural pearls on a beautiful necklace I am privileged to wear. This is my love letter to you all.

Start at the Beginning – Family – Thank You

Thank you, Mom, for your consistent and loyal love, no matter what. You taught me to distinguish between anger and love when you said to my teenage self, "Mary Catherine, I love *you*, but this behavior I do not love. It must stop." Thank you, too, for your willingness to challenge your own thinking and assumptions as it taught me to challenge mine. Thank you for always being there, and for being one of my best friends in adulthood. Even though I bristle a little at it, thank you for still saying, "Call or text me when you get home."

Daddy, though you have been gone more than half my life now, I carry your hardy laugh in my heart. Your belief in me may be your greatest gift and legacy to me, along with encouraging me to use my voice even when it irritates others or goes against the grain. When I shared a goal or talked about something I wanted to go for, your variations of the question, "What do you need to do to make that happen?" still make me believe I can take on bodacious challenges, like writing this book. Your lessons unfold like time-release medicine. I miss you more than I can ever explain.

Frank, thank you for your commitment to our relationship. Our adult sibling relationship is a treasured friendship that is filled with great comfort and authenticity. I appreciate all your love, support and big brother advice . . . along with the all the fun! Your generosity and kindness are dear gifts too and carry forward Daddy's Spirit. Through all manner of celebration and hardship (individually and collectively as a family), we are there for each other, and in it together. I am grateful and proud to call you brother.

Both my grandmothers were women of great faith who focused on love and relationships. Each sought in her own way to provide a positive environment, and each one made you think you were their very favorite person on earth! Thank you for instilling a reverence for people and Spirit; and an optimism that assumes positive intent and outcome even in the worst of circumstances. I only knew my maternal grandfather (the other died before my parents married). Grandad, thank you for demonstrating the power of saying yes when someone asks for help. I also learned a great deal about discipline from you—not by way of punishment, but in witnessing the way you honored your word and commitments.

My extended family of aunts, uncles and cousins—I thank you for your love and care. We were lucky to live close enough to gather for holidays and share in milestones like graduations, birthdays, marriages and summer vacations. You are all a backdrop of those formative years. As adults, gathering around tables today, we laugh about our shared fun times and honor with reverence the more serious times around illness and death. At the heart of it all, we celebrate love and family. I celebrate you.

Oh, the Joy of Friendship!

I am blessed with many circles of friends. The first such group of girlfriends I've known since first and second grade—Kelli, Laurie, Linda, Patti, Stephanie, Sheri! Thank you, my Port Arthur 6, for: making me laugh all day long, holding my hand as I cried over silly boys and as I lay in a hospital bed for two weeks recovering from the train wreck. I am so grateful we still get together. And Linda, I cannot imagine not having grown up next door to you. Your qualities of grit and heart make you one of my sheroes.

Thank you to The Goddesses—Anne, Barb, Connie, Connie, Darlene, Deb, Flint, Jena, Kiyomi, Lea, Maria, Tawnya, Tamara, Veronica. I love that we are famous to our other friends! Thank you for showing up in my life for twenty-plus years; for gathering in full moon rituals when it was way too cold to be outside and when we overflowed small living rooms; for coming together to celebrate the good, grieve the losses, heal the pain and support the striving. Thank you for your love and wise counsel.

Connie S, who knew thirty-five years ago, as tap dancing college roommates, we'd be the true sisters we are today? We are bonded like sisters as evidenced by the way we work through our disagreements and finish each other's sentences. Your ability to appreciate is second to none, and I am deeply grateful in how you see the good parts of me when I cannot. You make me stronger. Thank you.

Veronica, you didn't like me when we first met and I'm glad you decided to overcome your first line objections! I'm so grateful to have walked a path of spiritual depth and magic with you by my side. You inspire and challenge me in all the best ways as I marvel at your capacity to "get stuff done!" I appreciate your mix of wisdom, candor, tenderness and empathy.

Thank you to my tribe of coach and coach training colleagues around the globe. You nourish my innate curiosity, intuition, and need for meaningful conversation. You also challenge my assumptions and conditioning. In particular, thank you to Cynthia Calluori, Cynthia Loy Darst, Susan Carlisle, Camilla Rogers, Ron Renaud, Janet Keller, Hope Langner and Jim Patterson. (Dammit, Jim, you departed planet earth too soon.)

The Blessing of Mentors

I believe I am the woman I am today because of the three power-house women mentors I was lucky to have in my mid-twenties into my early thirties. Without each one of you, a piece of my puzzle would still be missing.

Thank you to my acting coach and often director, Maria Gobetti, for your belief in my talent. You pushed me beyond self-imposed limitations, type casting and taught me to work around the system. Perhaps most importantly, you invited me to see myself accurately in the dressing room mirror. Thank you for having confidence in me to step fully into the personas of various characters onstage. And thank you for sharing your story of healing when I was so sick.

Diane Miller, thank you for seeing my power and potential. You helped me to channel them for good. You taught me to be a guide and spiritual teacher for others—thank you, even though I was mad when you said I couldn't participate in your group again until I started my own! You demonstrated and modeled how to get things done in the non-profit world (and life). Thank you for all the escapades in Sacramento's hallowed legislative halls with our advocacy work for women. And most of all, for all the laughter along the way!

Laura Whitworth, you left this earth too soon, yet your impact on the world of Coaching and Coach Training, is very alive. You challenged me to transform from artist and actress into becoming a woman running her own business; into a woman who believes she is smart; into a woman who helps others transform their lives. Your belief in my capacity to stretch myself encourages me to keep stretching today. Thank you also for having a tender place in your heart for me to find refuge.

Nobody Writes a Book by Herself!

To my Kimchees writing group—Jeff Jacobson, Kim Fowler, Lauren Powers and Mary Reynolds Thompson—thank you. Your honest feedback, championing me forward when I wanted to throw in the towel, your saying it is okay to rest and insisting I didn't rest too long, all contributed to the completion of this book.

I love and respect each of your writing styles, and the subjects you wade into. You teach and inspire me each week.

To Mary Reynolds Thompson, my coach and editor, you have made me a better writer and I am so grateful for your deep intelligence. Your hard truths about what wasn't working in this manuscript helped me grow in my vulnerability and shake off the shackles of 'protecting' others who are a part of my story. Now, those parts of the story are like jewels because of your care, love, commitment and countless hours of editing.

Thank you dear Flint. Your writing genius simultaneously invites and challenges me to dig deeper, to find brevity in my long-windedness, to allow my poetry out. Thank you for your encouragement and belief in my writing . . . and in me.

Thank you to Cherry Hepburn of Putnam & Smith Publishing. For saying "Yes!" to publishing this book, and even more for saying, "I love it!" and "You have great style," after reading the manuscript with comments and editing notes still in the margins. Thank you Michelle Radomski for a meaningful book cover and beautiful layout. Thank you Jolie Margulies for being able to capture my essence with your incredible photography. Thank you Sheila Kennedy for copy editing, ensuring that I said what I meant and that the grammar and punctuation did, too!

The Village

Thank you to my coaching clients for trusting me with your dreams, hearts, psyches and lives. You individually and collectively have influenced my journey and helped me evolve my own work as I walk my talk. It has been an honor to walk beside you.

ACKNOWLEDGMENTS

Thank you to those that support my business, and me in my business! Joie Gharrity, Caren Glasser, Jenn Cass, Elenor Grafenthien, and all those that have assisted me formally and informally.

The Men of My Life

Thank you for loving me. Thank you for all the fun, romance, passion, laughter, conversation, and yes even the tears and heartache. I learned important life lessons from all of you, as well as learning more about myself. Thank you for walking the journey with me. May your life have been enhanced because of my time in it—I know mine is because of you.

Spirit

I am ever grateful for my ever-deepening, ever-widening, ever-affirming relationships to my own Higher Spirit, to my Future Self JoyFullLight, to Glinda my Guardian Angel and the host of Guides and Spirits that support my evolution. When I am the most lost, you help me get found. When I am doubtful, your words restore faith. When I am the loneliest, saddest, and most forlorn, you open a space of worthiness and love inside me.

To those I thanked by name, and to the countless others who have made my world a better place, I wish for each of you the joy, love, faith, courage, and kindness you have shown me.

And So It Is.

About the Author

Cat Williford is a modern-day goddess helping women around the globe to unmask their deep feminine wisdom and authentic voice. A connecter of diverse worlds, she fuses her own hard-won body wisdom with the knowledge of her Texas surgeon father's western medicine. The result is a holistic experience that nurtures vulnerability and strength. A master certified coach who received one of the first professional coaching credentials in the United States, Cat is also a keynote speaker and founder of The Modern Goddess series of workshops, ceremonies, and retreats. She has appeared coaching live on ABC's talk radio, and the *Los Angeles Times* dubbed her, "serene . . . with corporate polish and carefree humor."

Cat's signature program, The Authenticity Advantage™, is a uniquely powerful system to unmask women's stories, heartfelt vulnerabilities, and hardy resilience. Her vulnerability and willingness to tell it straight like a shot of tequila is part of her Texan charm. Cat's book, *The Ovarian Chronicles*, details the story of how she lost sight of navigating her future as her body's knowing became secondary to someone else's desires and reality. Her vulnerable honesty gives women permission to get real, forgive, heal, and recover their own resilience.

Today, Cat lives on the beach of Ventura, CA where she hunts for nautilus shells, dances to 1970's music in her living room and delights in moonlight sparkles on the ocean.

To learn more about Cat and her work, please visit: www.catwilliford.com.

We invite you to join Cat on her socials:

f Cat Williford

f Cat's Group: The Sisterhood Circle Advantage

🐦 @Catwilliford

in Cat Williford

Sign up for Cat's newsletter and gratis tools on her website: www.catwilliford.com